IT'S FUN TO HAVE A PONY

To Heather from Nannie
July 6th 1961.

MERRIE, PHILIP AND DAVY OFF TO THE FIELD

IT'S FUN
TO HAVE A PONY

How Three Children chose their Ponies and the many interesting things they did with them

By

PHYLLIS HINTON
Editor of "Riding"

WITH ILLUSTRATIONS BY MAURICE TULLOCH

WARD, LOCK & CO., LIMITED
LONDON, MELBOURNE AND CAPE TOWN

MADE IN ENGLAND

PRINTED IN GREAT BRITAIN BY
D. R. HILLMAN & SONS, LTD., FROME

CONTENTS

PLATES

DRAWINGS

DIAGRAMS

AUTHOR'S NOTE

GRATEFUL acknowledgements are due to Major Walker of the Wimbledon Equitation School, who took so much trouble over the photographs included in this book and to whom the three ponies who take part in them belong.

They are Rusty, a chestnut ridden by Richard Carreras, the skewbald Paintbox, ridden by his twin sister Montse, and the grey Llcan-Bach, ridden by David Jarvis. The first two riders were nine years of age when the photos were taken, and David eleven. All three are Pony Club members and take part in rallies.

These photos are used to illustrate various points, but the drawings and pictures by Maurice Tulloch are actually of Merrie with her pony Sambo, Philip with Alex and Davy with Mayflower.

P.H.

Merrie's dream pony

CHAPTER I

WANTED—A PONY

"YOU each want a pony," said Uncle Joe, looking at Philip and Esmeralda rather thoughtfully. "Now suppose you tell me why?"

Philip, who was eleven years old, looked rather surprised—he wanted a pony so much that he was more occupied with his feelings than with the reasons which prompted them. Esmeralda, who was eight, had plenty to say, however.

"Because it'll be fun, because I love Patsy's pony" (Patsy was a neighbour), "because I want to do the things they do in the Pony Club—because——"

"That's enough," said Uncle Joe, laughing. "I've quite an idea why you want it, but I'd like to hear something from Philip."

Philip looked rather strained—there were so many reasons he wanted a pony and some of them were hard to define. Eventually he said: "I'd like to get to know him, and how to ride him, and perhaps hunt or get across country."

Uncle Joe looked extremely pleased. "How right you are, my boy. First things first. Get to know your pony and there's not much you can't do." He seemed to fall into a brown study.

"I thought perhaps we could find one which we could get hold of somehow, and keep it in a field and Merrie could look after it during the term while I'm at school," said Philip. He really wanted a pony for each of them, but one had to make a start somewhere and their joint savings would not go very far.

Uncle Joe came out of his brown study. "I am going to make a bargain with you both," he said. "Mind you, it's got to be kept. Any funny business and there'll be trouble. Think very carefully about it before you accept it."

Two pairs of bright eyes watched him intently and Philip and Merrie waited anxiously for him to come to the point.

"Providing you will both take the trouble to learn all about ponies, different kinds of ponies and where they come from, how to ride them and look after them properly when they are sick or well, I will give you each a pony and you shall choose it for yourself."

Even Uncle Joe's solid body was nearly knocked sideways by the impact of Merrie's wild delight. She flung herself upon him, both arms round his neck, kissing him and crying out with excitement at the same time. "Darling Uncle Joe, how thrilling, oh yes! oh yes! 'course we'll learn all about them. I want a black-and-white one with a long tail that will gallop and gallop and gallop."

Philip was much quieter. He did not show any of the extravagant pleasure which had thrown Merrie into such a tiz-woz. But anyone who knew him would realize he was deeply moved. "Thank you, sir," he said. "Thank you very much, sir. It's—it's awfully good of you."

Uncle Joe smiled at them both. "There's one thing I've forgotten to say. When you can both ride yourselves and you *know* your ponies, you must teach Foozalum—on Merrie's pony, I should think." Foozalum was their small brother, four years younger than Merrie and called Foozalum after a favourite fairy story and because he was apt to get a little confused at times.

"Fooze won't be any good," said Merrie firmly, though all she had done herself was to crawl off and on good-tempered ponies and be led about by small friends for short rides.

"Now go and get us each a lemonade," said Uncle Joe, "and let's sit down here in the shade, and we'll see what kind of a pony we are going to choose—or try and choose, because ponies vary nearly as much as people, both in character and body. No, Merrie, you may not rush off and tell Patsy all about it—I can see that's what you are aching to do."

Merrie looked a little shame-faced and followed Philip in his search for the lemonade. When they returned they found their uncle waiting with a pencil and paper.

"Now it may seem dull and unexciting to get down to facts," he said, "but that's not the case at all. It is much more interesting if you know why you do a thing. Philip, you begin by describing the pony you want."

Philip looked thoughtfully at the ground. "Well, he must be pretty strong," he said. "I shall want to keep him for a few years. And he must be able to jump, and—and twist about in games or out hunting."

"Well, to find a pony like that you must look for a lot of things. To be pretty strong and able to carry you for a few years, during which time you will probably grow a great deal yourself, you must have a pony which is well proportioned—not too long in one direction and short in another. And to be handy for jumping and 'twisting about' he should be a fairly alert little chap, but *not* over-excitable or he'll waste his energy and make silly mistakes, and he should be well balanced, all his muscular force gathered together ready to be used, like a dancer or an athlete."

Philip looked thoroughly interested—all this made sense to him. Merrie was interested chiefly because she was surprised, never having given a thought to this angle of choosing a pony.

"Well now," said Uncle Joe, "I'll tell you the kind of ponies I think we should look for, and then we'll discuss where we are likely to find them. We'll begin with you, Miss," and he put his arm round the eight-year-old, stocky little Merrie.

"I don't want you to begin riding on a 'green' pony, one who can't help to teach you because it doesn't know anything itself. You are much too impatient a puss, anyway. You'd drive the pony mad with your impatience, because it would not understand you, and I

11

expect you'd do each other a lot of harm, perhaps have a nasty accident.

"No, the pony we want for you should stand no more than twelve hands two inches—a 'hand' is four inches—should be about your own age, eight, or older; must be a fairly hardy sort that you will not have to worry about too much: and that won't be too nervy or easily upset: is not too thick through the body to push your legs out of position and perhaps help widen your own little hips: or too narrow, so that you feel unsafe when it moves or turns suddenly and quickly; must not have a heavy head badly put on or an over-short or over-long neck, because that will make it difficult for you to learn to use your hands properly: and should not have flat withers, though that is not the most vital thing to consider.

"The withers are the highest fixed point in a horse or pony—his head is higher, but that moves up and down—and they are formed where the top ends of the shoulder bones meet. Well laid back shoulders help to keep the saddle in place and to see good withers in front of you gives you a nice feeling of stability. They help you when you are mounting, too.

"Apart from all this about your pony's looks, we must make sure he has a nice temperament, friendly, trustworthy. And that he is sure-footed."

For once, Merrie had nothing to say. She was too busy assimilating all these facts, which bore little relation to the picture of flowing mane and galloping hooves she had conjured up for herself.

Uncle Joe gave her a gentle dig in the ribs. "So much for what we expect of the pony," he said. "Now what about yourself?"

"*Me?*" asked Merrie, completely thunderstruck.

"Yes, *you*. If you want the best of your pony you've got to give something in exchange, you know. Fair do's. First, you must look after him right, then you must learn to ride him the right way, and then you, too, must have a nice temperament, be friendly and trust-worthy—treat him as a pal, think of him before yourself."

This fresh angle shook Merrie still more. She had merely looked upon ponies as the providers of fun. You patted them because they were dears, but you did not bother very much about them.

"Most things that go wrong between pony and rider have their cause in the rider, not the pony," said Uncle Joe. "Few people stop to think about that, and just make matters worse. But we'll see about that later. Now we've got Philip's pony to think of.

"He'll want one another hand higher, for preference, if it is going to last him some years, say between thirteen and fourteen hands roughly, though he could quite well ride a smaller one for a little while yet. But as Merrie will be having a smaller one, Philip may as well have a bigger.

"A nice boy's hunter type, I think, if we can get it, and something that can live out most of the year. He must have some of the same points as I described for Merrie's pony, though on a bigger scale, of course.

"As to age—I am not so convinced that he must be eight or over. We'll see. Philip has a different temperament from Merrie, as well as being three years older, and he and his pony might perhaps do a bit of learning together."

CHAPTER II

PUZZLE—FIND THE PERFECT PONY

FINDING the perfect pony, or indeed the finding of any perfect thing, takes time. Merrie, I am afraid, looked upon it as time wasted. She wanted her very own pony-to-be to appear instantly as if by magic, but there were many interesting, exciting and sometimes disappointing things to be done before this could happen.

They all pored over the advertisements of ponies for sale in *Horse & Hound*, they asked their friends if they knew of any good ponies outgrown by their riders, they considered an expedition to the nearest auction sales at Gorsebridge or a visit to the local dealer's yard.

Uncle Joe said he thought that if they could get a friendly pony for Merrie, which was used to children and recommended by someone they knew, that would be ideal, but if such a one was not available, he would like to find her a good native pony.

"You see," he said, "if we could find you a real Welsh or Dartmoor pony he'd be just the right size for some years, he can live out, which will be a cheaper and easier way to keep him, and he'll be sure-footed, hardy and clever. Or perhaps we could find you a nice little chap from the New Forest."

Merrie did not seem to be listening. She had her eyes glued to *Horse & Hound*. "Oh, Uncle, please, please can't I have this one?" she asked, and read part of the advertisement aloud—she could read very well for her age. "*High-class show pony for sale at reasonable price to good home. Has won many first prizes and championships and never been out of the money.*"

"It may be a wonderful pony," said Uncle Joe, "or it may be a nervy, unhappy, cunning little beast, sickened by too many shows. Let me tell you, my girl, you may graduate on to a show pony some day, but you're not going to start that way. You are going to learn how to look after and groom and ride your pony first, then how to

14

prepare him and yourself for the show-ring, not the other way round."

Merrie looked slightly dashed, and Uncle Joe smiled at her. "Don't worry," he said, "you won't have much longer to wait. I've answered one or two of those advertisements and I've written to the secretaries of some of the pony societies, but while we are waiting we'll go to a little pony farm I've heard about and just take a look round."

"Now?" asked Merrie.

"Now," said Uncle Joe.

They ran off to fetch their coats and to obtain permission from their parents, who seemed to know just what was going to happen, and bundled into Uncle Joe's old car, called the Black Beetle because of its ability to get over the ground and to slide in and out of the most impossible places.

"Shall we see a pony for me as well as one for Merrie?" Philip inquired as they "beetled" along.

"You never know," said Uncle Joe, "but we can pick up a few tips, anyway. Watch all the ponies and tell me what you think of each one."

After about an hour Uncle Joe stopped the Beetle at the top of a hill and took the children into an adjoining field. "Look!" he said.

Standing on the crest of the hill, they gazed across a wide valley with rolling green hills on the far side and a little stream running through the centre of it, with trees growing near it. Several fields were full of ponies of all ages and sizes, ranging from silvery greys to blacks and browns. The sun was shining on them, and in the distance one or two foals were at play, while their dams ate grass.

Even Merrie was speechless before this realization of her dreams. Philip gazed at them very intently, a little smile on his lips.

Uncle Joe laughed outright, swept them back into the car and set sail for the little stone house on the far side of the valley.

"Some ponies for the children?" said the owner of this little house, Mrs. Matherston, when they arrived. "Yes, *my* children are schooling one or two this very minute, and there are plenty more in the fields. Come and see."

15

In a pleasant paddock just behind the stables a little girl, smaller than Merrie, was riding a rough-coated young pony, and a boy was jumping a lovely little grey, about thirteen hands in height. (A hand being four inches, the grey was about four feet four inches high at the withers.)

Another and older girl came running towards them leading a lovely chestnut pony, with a cream-coloured mane and tail. Merrie patted it on its soft little muzzle politely enough, but she kept turning towards the shining silver-grey who cantered round the field so light-heartedly, bounding over the jumps with the greatest enjoyment.

"Not a beginner's pony," said Uncle Joe, smiling at her.

"He is a very gentle pony," said Mrs. Matherston. "I believe that with a little care at first she would soon learn to manage him. Bring Silvo here, Peter," she called to the boy. The little grey came towards them as swiftly and lightly as a snowflake.

Peter jumped off and Uncle Joe lifted Merrie on, a look of pure bliss on her face. She spoke to him and patted his neck and Peter led him away at a walk, then told her to take hold of his mane and ran a few steps. Silvo moved so easily at the trot that Merrie, who had once or twice practised this pace on friends' ponies, could hardly believe it. Could, oh could, this dream pony ever become hers?

"I am afraid he is too perfect a pony for this young lady at the moment," said Uncle Joe, knowing full well how Merrie was feeling, though she kept her eyes on Silvo. "Better tell me how much he costs, first of all—a hundred pounds? Oh, I've no doubt he's worth it, and I've no doubt he'll fetch three or four times as much after he has been shown once or twice. But I am afraid it is quite out of the question."

Merrie slid dejectedly to the ground, and followed her uncle and Philip round the fields. Nothing seemed to go right. The less expensive animals were too young or too small or too big, the others too dear. She became very sad because she began to feel she would never have a pony.

Presently they came to a paddock in which all kinds of ponies seemed to be turned out, and which looked a little different, less gay, less buoyant than the lovely show ponies, jumping ponies, ponies for export and ponies for hunting which they had just seen. One or two were very thin, others moved a shade stiffly.

Mrs. Matherston leant over the gate and whistled softly, and a funny little dun-coloured pony with a short tail came towards her carrying his head up and his ears pricked, but limping.

She took Merrie's hand, opened it out flat and laid a piece of carrot on the palm. "Don't stick your thumb out," she said, flattening it against the side, "or Punch might nip it off in mistake for the carrot, and hold your hand quite flat." She turned to Uncle Joe.

"This, I must tell you, is the Field of Recovery. Some of these ponies have had a hard time and I buy them and bring them here to get well and happy again. Punch is a very old jumping pony. He has won a lot of prizes, but his late owner made him go on and on long after he had the strength to do it. One day he crashed into a triple bar and he has been lame in the shoulder ever since."

"Are you looking after him for his owners?" inquired Uncle Joe.

Merrie finds Sambo

Philip was stroking the pony, and running his hand very gently over his shoulder and front legs to feel for swellings.

Mrs. Matherston smiled. "Oh no," she said. "Poor Punch will never again be a consistent winner, jumping in the show ring. He's 'had it', I'm afraid, though I think that when he's better he'll make a good 'nursemaid' for a year or two. I bought him cheap to give him a chance of recovery and perhaps a year or two at an easy job—I know him to be a great little trier and he's earned a bit of respect and kind treatment."

"Hardly a beginner's 'nursemaid' pony if he has spent many years jumping for his living," said Uncle Joe, looking round to see if Merrie had now decided she wanted Punch. "Probably he's got a mouth like iron by now—where on earth has Merrie got to, Philip?"

To everyone's surprise Merrie seemed to have disappeared completely and silently while they were talking—her silence was the most surprising thing of all.

"One of your invalids has eaten the little puss!" declared Uncle Joe.

"Look!" exclaimed Mrs. Matherston, pointing to the far end of the field, where it dipped towards the stream.

Just emerging from a tangle of shrubby trees appeared a little black object with pricked ears, and a saucy face nearly hidden by a long and tangled mane, balanced at the other end by an even longer and more luxuriant tail, which only just missed the ground.

This apparition was accompanied by Merrie, whose arm was round its neck, and who looked equally small and saucy. They advanced unconcernedly towards the group who awaited them. Punch wandered off to eat grass.

"What have you got there?" inquired Uncle Joe. Mrs. Matherston, smiling, said nothing, but waited to hear their comments. The black pony looked at them with some interest and did not attempt to eat grass; Merrie kept her arm round its neck, her little face very intent. She seemed to have difficulty in knowing what to say—very unusual for Merrie. At last "This one"—a hesitation, then in one breath: "I want this one much, much more than the hundred-pound one."

To everyone's surprise Uncle Joe did not ask how much it would cost. He winked at Mrs. Matherston. "Now, my girl, and you,

18

too, Philip, just tell me all about this pony. We've got to know his age and his good and bad points. I know you fancy him and I don't blame you, but you must show me all the things you've noticed about him."

This was rather too much for Merrie. She did not know how to say quickly that she loved the pony because he was so small but so strongly made, that the look in his large and generous eye, the way he carried himself made her think that his independent little nature and hers would bring about plenty of adventures for both of them, that his flowing mane and tail and coat not only seemed beautiful to her, but as if Nature had endowed him with the necessary equipment to fend for himself, which increased her respect for him. It is doubtful if she had ever thought all these things out, although they were the sum total of what she felt.

Philip came to her assistance. "He looks all of a piece," he said, which puzzled Merrie, but Uncle Joe gave a laugh and exclaimed: "Very well put. Lots of ponies look as if their front and their quarters were not cut out of the same pattern, or as if another pony's rear half were tacked on to their front half by mistake. Not only ugly, but doesn't usually work—it's too unbalanced."

Uncle Joe turned to Mrs. Matherston. "Can you spare us the time for a little chat about your pony?" he asked. "I don't know, of course, but it looks to me like a Dartmoor."

"Oh yes," said Mrs. Matherston, "Sambo is a Dartmoor all right. The trouble was——"

"Hush," begged Uncle Joe. "Don't tell us a thing. Let's see what we can find out for ourselves."

CHAPTER III

SIZING UP SAMBO

WHAT TO LOOK FOR WHEN BUYING A PONY

"WE won't keep you too long," said Uncle Joe to Mrs. Mather-ston. "The children shall study their ponies properly when they've got them at home. But I'd like to give them an idea of how to size a pony up before they decide if they really want it or not."

"I'm enjoying it, too," said Mrs. Matherston, smiling.

"Well, there's something we've always got to find out if we are buying a pony," declared Uncle Joe. "And that's his age. Maybe it will disappoint us, maybe it will be just right, but whatever the case we must know it.

"Take a look at this grand little fellow, children. He's not show-ing signs of wear, except for—but we'll come to that in a minute. Glance at his front legs—his little joints don't look big, and he's not 'up on them', which would mean that they were worn and stiffened and his weight thrown forward. He is quite alert, nice and plump and looking well in his coat.

"What do I mean by that? No, I do not just mean that he has been well-groomed—come and feel his skin and see how easily it moves backwards and forwards over his bones, not taut like a drum and sticking to them. See the healthy glow on it—I grant you that it would shine a lot more if Sambo was living in a stable and was properly groomed every day, but it is bright and alive, not dull or dead as it would be if he were an old pony out of condition—or a young pony out of condition for that matter. And it lies fairly flat despite the lack of grooming. If he were cold, or not well, it might be 'staring'—all the hairs sticking out on end like a soft brush.

"Now let's look at his teeth. Come on, Philip, I know you've been mugging it up a bit. Tell us how old Sambo is."

Philip came forward rather doubtfully, spoke to Sambo and very

Holding up a good front foot, nicely proportioned with a strong sole and well-defined frog (the piece which stands out and has a cleft in it) to act as a buffer.

Here is Anne Bullen on a thoroughbred show pony with a fine neck, withers, and shoulder—this ensures that the rider has 'plenty in front of her' to quote a horsey term, and 'a good length of rein.'

A nicely made, alert pony with his rider sitting well. He has a fine head, well set on to a good neck, which in turn is correctly attached to a deep shoulder. You can see that his withers leave little to grumble about, his forearm is strong, knee flat, cannon bone short, fetlocks and pasterns good, and feet well proportioned. His elbow is not too close to his body. He has a nice depth of girth, a strongly made back—perhaps a shade long behind the saddle—and a good hind leg with his hocks under him.

gently took hold of his lower jaw on both sides just behind the front lower teeth, the incisors and the tusks, pressing it down a little and holding the top jaw steady with the other hand. He peered inside and fortunately Sambo was quite happy about this inspection, but he did not give Philip very much time in which to look.

"I should think he was—rather old," said Philip doubtfully.

"Afraid you're quite right, old boy. Tell us why you think it."

"Well, his teeth are rather long and they are beginning to slope outwards a bit, instead of upwards, and one of them has a mark at the side."

"All correct. A young pony's teeth grow straight up from the bottom jaw and down from the top, and certain marks gradually appear, which show till they are seven years old, when they start to disappear—I'll draw you a picture when we get home. As a pony gets older his top and bottom teeth begin to slant outwards, and when he is ten or eleven an upper tooth at the side—the upper corner incisor—has a little groove or mark which starts near the gum and gradually grows downward. It is usually half-way down at fifteen, right down at twenty, the top half disappears at twenty-five, and it has grown right out of the tooth by thirty—if the pony is still alive. Actually, Sambo's is not very far advanced, and I don't think he's more than twelve or thirteen—nothing to worry about in a Dartmoor, as most native ponies are long-lived.

"Now, having decided on his age, we'll go on a bit further. Come on, tell me something about him yourselves. What about his head, Merrie?"

Merrie was still strangely quiet. She could not think of much to say about Sambo's head, except that she liked it. At last: "He has lovely big eyes."

"You're right, a generous eye—no little piggy, cunning eyes for us. And a really jolly little head, nicely pricked ears and big nostrils. The last thing I want for you is a heavy-headed pony, and Sambo's head is set nicely on to his neck—more diagrams explaining it all when we get home—and a good neck, narrowing where it joins his head, deepening as it reaches his shoulders, joining them nicely, and not looking as if it were 'put on upside down', which makes it difficult for the muscles to work properly.

21

"And a deep shoulder, deep from front to back—wide would be the wrong word—and joining together to form narrow withers, which stand up just a little way in front of the saddle.

"A grand little chest, not too wide or too narrow, in proportion to the rest of his body, and a strong forearm and elbow not too tight against his side, so that he can stride out—yes, I mean elbow!

"The point or joint at the top of the front leg where it joins the body is supposed to correspond with our elbow, then we get a nice, muscley forearm, and a strong, flat knee (or wrist). Next is the cannon bone, running from the knee to the fetlock. The shorter and bigger it is the better. And see how nicely Sambo's fits at the knee, not, as it were, dipping under it at the back, which is called 'tied-in'. Nor does it seem to give a bit, so that his knee looks as if it were bending, which is called 'over at the knee' and which, strange as it may seem, is not such a bad fault as being either 'tied-in' or else 'back at the knee'.

"A nice, sloping pastern between the fetlock and coronet, which is the top of his hoof. Good little feet, not exaggeratedly sloping or too upright and boxy-looking. Good, well developed, clean frogs right against the ground—the frog is the spongy bit with a sort of channel or cleft in it between the heel (it is at the bottom of the heel) and the sole, which is the flat or slightly concave underneath part. The sole reaches to the wall, which is the outside part all round the foot. Out of sight and well protected are the bones.

"Look how Sambo's feet match one another. It is always a good thing if the front feet match each other, and the hind feet are a matching pair, too. One should not be narrower or bigger than the other, or one turned in or out.

"Now let's stand back and take a good look at Sambo. Time you said something, Philip."

"Well," said Philip, "he's got a fine, strong back."

"Yes, a real strong back and loins and he'd carry quite a bit of weight without sagging in the middle. I hate a weak-looking back. Sambo has a good depth of girth, too—I mean the part just in front of where the girth goes. Plenty of room for heart and lungs here. He's got a nice body altogether, not too round and wide and not too mean and narrow.

22

"Nicely proportioned, strong-looking quarters, not sloping too much, and strong, flat hocks, which are supposed to correspond with our ankles. No puffiness or swellings or hard lumps anywhere here, and he stands four square, with his hocks under him—doesn't seem to trail them behind when he moves, either. A horse or pony is badly built who 'leaves his hocks behind him'. It stands to reason he must have his wheels or supports where they will take the weight.

"Hello, hello, what's this? Not so good, I'm afraid. Anyone seen what I've seen?"

Merrie looked doubtful. Philip pointed to Sambo's two hind fetlock joints, one of which was larger than the other. "They're not a pair," he said.

Uncle Joe smiled. "That's one way of looking at it. Actually one of those joints is a good bit bigger than the others and looks as if it had become hard or calloused. A nasty blemish and one which time won't cure, I'm afraid. Can you tell us about it, Mrs. Matherston?"

"Yes, I'm afraid Sambo had rather a nasty accident. That's why he is in the Field of Recovery. A little girl had him who was very excitable and fond of enjoying herself, but never stopped to think much about poor Sambo. She would tear along the hard road to gymkhanas on him and in between events she would never get off and rest his back, but would canter about amusing herself and showing off.

"Then she went to boarding school and he was turned out in a field with no companion, a thing which most horses hate, though they show it in different ways. Well, Sambo is a grand little jumper, most Dartmoors are, and his way of showing it was to jump out of the field, but unfortunately there was a low iron railing on the landing side, which he could not see, and he caught it with his hind leg, giving this joint an awful rap."

"What happened then?"

"Well, he was laid up for a long time, and then I saw him at a sale, bought him and put him out in the field till I'd made up my mind what to do with him."

Uncle Joe grunted. "Well, we've looked at him and now I suggest

23

we *feel* him. Come along, Philip, run your hand down his front leg and see what you find there."

Philip spoke to Sambo as he went up to him, as Uncle Joe had always impressed it upon him never to approach or touch or even pass by a horse without speaking to it first, as horses are very easily startled and may lash out from pure nervousness. He ran his hand down his front leg, over his fetlock joint, feeling the pastern and the top of the coronet for any hard lumps which might be ring bone or side-bones.

A little uncertain, he felt the back of the leg a second time and then said: "There's a small lump here, Uncle."

Uncle Joe bent forward and ran his fingers over the place pointed out by Philip.

"Well done," he said, thoroughly pleased with Philip for finding it out. "There's a splint here. Nothing to worry about, though, as it's not in a bad position. Except that they don't look nice if they are big enough to be seen, splints don't matter terribly once they are formed, unless they are just under the knee and likely to interfere with its action. They are to be found on the little splint bone which runs up behind the cannon bone."

After a little further examination Mrs. Matherston called one of her children to bring a halter and run Sambo up and down for Uncle Joe to see how he moved—to see if he moved quite straight without turning his toes in or "plaiting" in a sort of circular movement with his front legs, to make sure he was quite sound everywhere and not stiff, and that he had a fair length of stride.

Then a saddle was put on his back and the little boy Merrie had watched jumping the grey pony walked, trotted, cantered and circled him for them. He did everything the boy asked very obediently, and Mrs. Matherston assured them he was perfectly sound in his wind. He certainly made no noise when breathing, as he cantered about, and his little flanks beat quite evenly when he was stopped. The movement is uneven when a pony is broken-winded.

The great moment arrived when the final decision had to be made. Uncle Joe looked thoughtfully at Merrie. "You shall choose," he said. "Sambo is a very nice pony with quite a number of years before him, though he certainly would be beaten by a younger pony

24

in the show ring—not that we can show him except in performance classes or gymkhana events, because the blemished joint would always prevent him from winning on his looks. He seems to be decently trained and to have good manners and the right temperament.

"He may go lame on that joint one day, though I think it would take more work than you are likely to give him to make that happen, but some slight accident would bring it about. The question is, would you rather have Sambo and his disadvantages or a more ordinary sort of pony without these disadvantages, for the same price?"

"Sambo," said Merrie.

CHAPTER IV

GETTING READY FOR THE RALLY

"I SEE our branch of the Pony Club is practising for the Inter-Club Tests at Willowcombe to-day," announced Uncle Joe a week later. "We'll pop over there and poor old Philip can have a look at the ponies and decide which type he'd like to have. Have you both got your membership badges?"

"Poor old Philip" was feeling somewhat envious of his sister, since Sambo had arrived but no pony had yet been found for him. Still, there had been plenty to do in connection with Sambo and he had become nearly as attached to the black pony as Merrie was.

Together they had cleaned out the old stable which was to be Sambo's home, climbed on the roof to make sure there were no tiles missing to let in the rain, repainted the swing door, out of the top half of which they hoped he would be able to poke his little head, though it seemed rather doubtful if he was tall enough.

Together they had made sure that the adjoining paddock, which he would share with Philip's pony when it arrived, had no weak places in the stout hedge surrounding it through which Sambo could creep, no loose strands of wire, or odd bits of galvanized iron on which he could injure himself. They noted with pride the trees which would help to provide shade in summer and shelter in winter and the little stream which skirted one end, from which he could always enjoy a drink of fresh running water.

They were thoroughly pleased with themselves, as if by their own efforts they had been able to provide his small lordship with a fitting kingdom.

Uncle Joe gave them a lecture on what they would have had to do if none of these necessities had been available, and set them to work to make a little manège in one corner of the field where they could practise their riding.

It consisted of a section about fifty-five yards long and perhaps thirty-five yards wide, roughly enclosed with sheep hurdles, in which he assured them they would have a lot of practice. He said that he might decide to fence it in properly and put up jumps at some time, or he might even take the hurdles away, leaving some short posts as markers, but that in any case he would have a cinder track laid down for bad weather, and some time, when they were a little more advanced, he would measure out an arena in which they could practise for the Pony Club tests.

When Sambo arrived, very black, very small, but completely self-contained and gazing with interest out of the long strands of his flowing mane which fell over his face, Merrie had embraced him fondly and desired to climb immediately upon his back.

But Uncle Joe had insisted that he should first be allowed to get used to his surroundings and be sustained by a refreshing drink and a meal.

He had no shoes as yet and although he could work perfectly well in the field unless it got hard and ridgy, Uncle Joe thought he had better be shod before taking him across rough country with the weight of fat Merrie on his back.

The blacksmith was a large, friendly man with curly hair as black as Sambo's coat and he had shown them how to pick up his feet.

"You speak to him and get him tranquil," said old Bill. "Then you stand close beside him. Always remember that the closer you are the less likely you are to get kicked. You run your hand down his leg and lift it upwards—most horses will pick their feet up fairly easily. If not, a little tap behind the knee with the edge of your hand should make them do it. And if you want to clean out his hind feet, don't pull the one on the outside inwards towards you, cross it over behind—outside—the leg he is standing on."

Old Bill had made them take a good look at Sambo's feet and watch him fit the shoe on carefully without paring away the frog and making sure that the shoe did not prevent it from touching the ground and carrying out its duty as shock absorber.

Sambo lived in the paddock, coming into the stable out of the way of the flies during the hot part of the day and Philip and Merrie took it in turns to groom him. His luxuriant mane was well brushed, but hardly combed at all, and Uncle Joe said that although later on

27

they might perhaps shorten it and tidy it up a little, for the moment they would leave it as it was, as it acted as such a protection to his head and eyes from both the glare and the flies.

They brushed him over every day with a stiff dandy brush, taking great care not to knock his hip or any of his joints with the point or back of the brush. There was sad trouble on the first day when Uncle Joe inspected Merrie's handiwork.

"What's this?" he said, feeling behind Sambo's lovely little ears. "And this—and this?" running his fingers into the cavern of his throat, behind his elbows, under his tummy just where the girth would go, and inside his legs.

Merrie looked crest-fallen. "I was afraid of hurting his little, soft ears," she said.

"Quite right," agreed Uncle Joe, smiling now. "Do them with the soft body brush, very gently, till you get the knack. But you must make a great point of doing just behind his ears where the head-piece of the bridle would go, because that is where there might be dried sweat which would easily rub into a sore place. And the same applies to his elbow and under his girth and inside his legs— there might be dried mud and muck and gravelly dust there, too, to make it even worse."

After brushing Sambo very thoroughly all over with the stiff dandy brush to get out any dirt, or sweat or scurf, they repeated the process with the softer, shorter bristled body brush, holding it in one hand, with the curry comb on which to clean it in the other, and changing hands as they changed sides, and not forgetting his mane and tail. They used the brush with a brisk swinging motion, over the pony and across the curry comb to clean the bristles, then back on to the pony again.

To do this thoroughly it was necessary to put plenty of energy into it, but it soon became a knack and ceased to tire them, and they learnt to avoid rough movements or the possibility of striking the pony with the brush.

When the main grooming was finished they wiped Sambo's eyes and nose and dock with a sponge wrung out of clean water, then rinsed it again and squeezed it dry, inspected his feet for stones, and to see that his shoes were firm, not loose or twisted, and that no nail

28

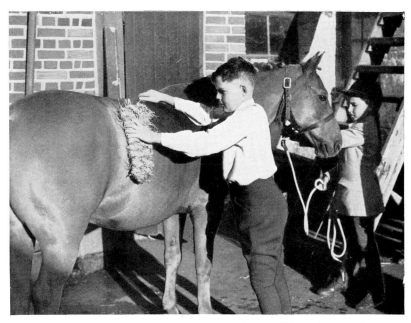

Using a hay wisp with a slapping movement, to give a polish, to improve the pony's muscle and circulation.

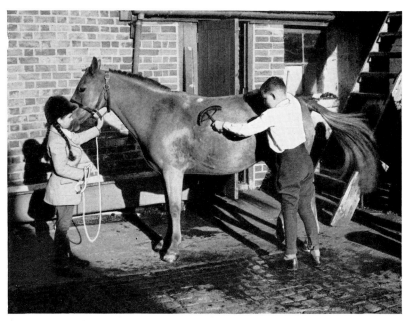

Using a scraper on a wet pony. It should be used with a sweeping, downward motion on the plumpest and most muscular parts and great care taken not to knock bones or joints.

Touching left toe with right hand while trotting.

Feeding time—the measure holds about 2½ lbs. of crushed oats, the armful of hay is enough for one meal for a 13 hands 2 ins. pony· The bucket of water must never be forgotten.

heads or clenches were sticking out; if they had been Uncle Joe would quickly have hammered them flat to make sure that they would not cause any sore places.

Merrie and Philip learned to pick out each foot with the hoof pick, being very careful not to injure the frog with the point of the pick, and to use the hook downwards, never to hook upwards towards themselves.

They then gave Sambo a rub over with a hay whisk, which they soon learnt to plait for themselves, or a clean stable rubber, to remove any flecks of dust, to give a good shine and—all grooming has this object in view—to massage and tone up the muscles all over his body, and stimulate the circulation, which helps the skin of both humans and horses to carry out its natural functions.

There was a little trouble over the grooming kit, as Merrie frequently lost hers in the straw, but this problem was solved by each having a little box and keeping their own tools in it. Uncle Joe supervised and saw to it that they were put away clean, and that the brushes were washed and thoroughly dried occasionally.

Carrying a saddle the comfortable way

It was decided that as Willow-combe was only a couple of miles away they would walk over, accompanied by Sambo, whom they could take it in turns to ride.

Merrie was a little saddened by the fact that Philip appeared to be getting on rather better than she was, chiefly because he seemed more able to remember all Uncle Joe's instructions, understand the reason for them and relate them to what he was doing, whereas she was so excited, so ready to worship Sambo and to feel the joy of the moment with such intensity that she was quite unable to concentrate on theory, to remember her instructions.

For all that, she and Sambo wandered about together in great contentment and seemed to understand each other very well, though what would have happened if any difficulty had arisen is a questionable point.

Philip put on Sambo's saddle and bridle. The saddle was placed a little far forward and then slid back, so as not to run any hairs the wrong way. He took good care to see it was in the right place, not forward enough to interfere with his shoulder action, or so far back that the girth was round the large part of his tummy and would therefore soon be displaced.

When Philip girthed it up he was rather surprised that he had to buckle it into a hole lower down the strap than before, but foolishly did not look for the reason. He did however make sure that the buckle was on the under flap of the saddle, not against the pony's flesh, where it might cut him.

Sambo was always very good about being bridled, practically putting his head into the bridle instead of trying to evade it. Philip placed the reins over his neck, placed his left hand under the little snaffle bit, holding the top of the head piece in his right hand and sliding the bit into his mouth and the head piece over his ears in one gentle, smooth motion, in the way demonstrated many times by Uncle Joe.

He had also told them many times that they must never do up the throat lash too tight, since if Sambo was cantering he needed more space to get his breath and too tight a throat lash might injure his wind. Neither must they have it ridiculously loose—they should be able to slide their hand comfortably between it and the jaw bone. And the browband must not be too tight, either.

Operations were held up by a loud cry from Merrie, who had noticed a slight lump under the flap of the saddle on her side. On inspection it turned out that Philip had done up the girth without looking to see if the under flaps were lying flat against the pony on both sides, and the end of this flap was doubled over under the girth, which explained why he had been obliged to buckle it a couple of holes lower than usual.

It would probably have caused a very sore place quite quickly, not only hurting Sambo but preventing them from riding him for several days.

However, at last they got going, Merrie actually remembering to gather the reins in her left hand, face her pony's tail when she put her left foot in the stirrup and hop round and up in one swinging motion, with her right hand placed over the seat of the saddle to start her off.

There was to be no riding lesson to-day, just a tour of inspection, so we will not go into that side of it, beyond saying that Uncle Joe, who was walking with them, reminded her to keep her heels down and her knees close to the saddle, pointing the way she was going, and to remember that Sambo's mouth was at the end of the reins and not wave her hands about.

It was a lovely sunny morning and they wandered along a pleasant lane, enjoying the soft sounds and sweet scents of the countryside until they came to a big field where between twenty and thirty ponies and their riders had already gathered together, as a preliminary to dividing into groups and practising for the Pony Club tests.

"Oh, Merrie, is that your new pony?" A small girl on a stocky little animal with a short neck and rather heavy head, came cantering up, stopping more by good luck than good management as the pony did not respond to her tugs on the reins.

This kind of pony usually has a bad mouth, particularly if they carry their heads low as this one did, and do not bend it or "bridle" at all.

Sambo was very good tempered and made no attempt to rush off with the other ponies, so Uncle Joe and Philip strolled a short way away, leaving Merrie to describe Sambo's purchase.

First of all a very lovely thoroughbred fourteen hands two inches pony passed them. "Too dear," said Uncle Joe. "And probably not as easy to look after as something with a bit less blood."

Then a nice grey Welsh-Arab cross, strongly made, swift moving and carrying its head in the proper place—not uncomfortably high, not down between its knees, not stuck out straight or tucked into

31

its chest. "That's a nice sort," admitted Uncle Joe. "A well-put-together pony, with a head and neck properly put on, nearly always has a good mouth because it is naturally well balanced and doesn't have any occasion to fight the bit, except in the hands of a particularly bad rider."

A very harnessy pony, rather heavy and inclined to bend its knee too much, next appeared. "Very useful," commented Uncle Joe. "But not my choice."

The next one was quite different and could be described as a "flat-catcher," which is the term used by dealers when speaking of a rather showy animal which attracts the attention of the inexperienced person, but which is not really very well-made.

This bright chestnut looked and moved very dashingly, but it was "on the leg"—its legs were too long for the size of its body, which was "shallow" into the bargain. A "shallow" horse has a body which is not strong or well-proportioned, but rather too narrow. Sometimes such horses also lack depth of girth and heart-room.

Three average ponies arrived, neither very good, nor very bad—none had a particularly long stride, or fine limbs, or made you feel that you loved them at sight, but all were nice, useful animals.

Suddenly a dark chestnut pony trotted by who made them stand and stare. A real boy's hunter, strongly made, with beautiful limbs and a very fine quality head. He moved so gallantly and in such a businesslike way that he seemed to make all the others look ordinary.

"The very thing," said Uncle Joe.

"I'll say he is," agreed Philip. And they went into a huddle, trying to think how they could get this particular pony. Or if not him, one like him.

His foot was caught in the stirrup and he was dragged along

CHAPTER V

MERRIE'S ADVENTURES

In the meanwhile, poor Merrie was having far more adventures than she had ever expected. The instructor, who was taking the small group of children in their practice for the elementary D test, called them over to one corner of the field, and from the far end a small boy came tearing towards them at a terrific bat.

The pony put in a playful bounce and he shot over its shoulder, but unfortunately his foot was caught in the stirrup and he was dragged along by the frightened animal, who dashed straight at Sambo, coming to a dead stop with its head on his quarters.

Sambo made a startled movement to get out of the way and Merrie fell forward on his neck. However, he raised his head, helping her to wriggle back into place, and stood still.

"David! Davy!" cried the instructor, running to him and catching

c

the pony's rein with one hand to prevent it dashing off again, while with the other she helped to disentangle him. "Are you all right?"

A red-headed little imp not much older than Merrie disentangled himself and displayed many green stains, a few scratches and a lop-sided and disarming smile, apologetic and very near to tears.

"Listen, children," said the instructor. "Let Davy's accident be a lesson to you. He's had such a lucky escape—a great deal luckier than he deserves, considering he should know better and considering the amount of damage he might have done to other people"—she looked at the interested Merrie. "Now, come on, David, tell us what you did wrong."

Davy regarded them with a seraphic smile. "I set her off much too quick," he volunteered, quite unashamed and apparently still remembering the thrill at the start.

"I'll never say a word to you about having a scamper *when* you can ride well enough to handle that fast little pony. Now it's just silly and selfish to do it. Even if you hadn't fallen off you couldn't have pulled her up and well you know it. What else was wrong?"

"My stirrup iron," said Davy, seeming to take this rather more seriously.

"Yes," said the instructor, whose name was Miss Brown. "Let's look at it—take it off the saddle and try your foot in it."

When Davy did this it was found that the stirrup iron was not only so wide that his foot slipped about in it, but it was so high that the foot would go right through and then upside down, as was the case when he fell. Crowning horror, a safety catch on the saddle which would not open, having been left up until it had become fixed in position, prevented the stirrup leather from slipping free. Had the safety catch been in good order, or been down, the stirrup would have come off and he would not have been dragged.

Having forced the catches down and replaced David on the saddle, Miss Brown turned to Merrie.

"What a very well behaved pony you have," she said. "Many ponies would have dashed off, or else would have kicked Davy's pony. You know, I suppose, that never in any circumstances is it really safe to ride too close to another pony's hindquarters, let alone arrive on top of them in the way Davy's Mayflower did?"

34

It was at this moment that Uncle Joe and Philip arrived, announcing that they had better be making tracks for home as Merrie was not really advanced enough to take part in the rally.

"I'll come, too," announced Davy.

"But you'll miss our practice," said Miss Brown. She looked at him thoughtfully, wondering if he had had more of a shake-up than she realized. "All right, David, your home lies in the same direction as the others. See what you can do about new irons before the next rally, and don't be so foolish another time."

Whistling to himself and crossing his stirrups in front of him, Davy rode off with them. Philip told Merrie about the pony he wanted so much.

"You'll never get him," said Davy helpfully and went on whistling, then added, "Not unless you pay the earth."

"Isn't he for sale?" asked Philip.

"Who does he belong to?" asked Uncle Joe.

"Do they love him so much?" inquired Merrie.

"Them—they'd sell anything for a price," said Davy, taking each question in turn and wasting no words. "Their name's Wideawake and they live at Sheepcote, miles away, and young Ted, he comes to the rallies in a car with a trailer. Love Rowan? Nah, they don't love him, but they like to own him."

"Doesn't look very hopeful," said Uncle Joe.

"There's ways and ways," said Davy, but could not be persuaded to say any more.

"Poor Rowan," said Merrie, thinking of the unloved but merely possessed pony—such an attitude did not seem a possibility to her, unless the owners were freaks, outside her understanding.

Philip said nothing, but seemed wrapped in thought.

"Better forget him," said Uncle Joe. "A grand sort and a real model, but we don't know much about him, beyond what we've seen to-day. We'll find you something else that won't cost as much and you shall train him yourself—I believe you'd make a job of it."

It must be said here that Philip had learnt something about riding at his preparatory school—one of the few schools where they kept their own ponies—whereas Merrie was a real beginner.

35

As they reached the gate leading to the stables, a small figure, much smaller than Merrie, ran towards and threw itself ecstatically upon Sambo, who gave it a friendly shove with his nose. This was the youngest member of the family, Foozalum, aged four, who just knew Sambo as an entrancing new discovery in a thoroughly good world.

Nobody took much notice of him as he was too occupied with Sambo to go near Davy's Mayflower, still an unknown quantity as far as they were concerned, whom he would not have been allowed to approach too carelessly. Davy had riveted their attention by saying, "Going to the sale to-morrow?"

"What sale?"

"Dartmoor ponies at Gorsebridge."

"Oh-h," a long drawn-out sigh of disappointment. "That's miles away."

"Not above thirty miles," said Davy. "Dad's going in the truck. Maybe he'll take you, if you'd like to come."

No one knew who Dad was, nor what the van was like, and no one cared very much. There was a chorus of "May we's" and promises by Philip to keep an eye on Merrie and by Merrie to behave sensibly. In the end it was agreed that they should meet Davy on the village green early the next morning with sandwiches in their pockets, prepared to spend the day at the sale.

Davy and Mayflower proceeded unconcernedly upon their way, Mayflower's reins loose on her bright chestnut neck, Davy whistling and light-heartedly enjoying the air and sunshine, the colour in the fields of ripening corn and wheat, and the soft sound of life in the hedgerows and trees.

"What kind of a pony is that?" asked Philip.

"I wonder why it is called Mayflower?" from Merrie.

Uncle Joe laughed. "You'll find all that out to-morrow, I'm sure. It's a very high-class pony with a lot of good blood in it, but a bit mixed in type and a bundle of nerves, I should think. Probably not a young pony, either—I expect there's a good story attached to it. Your little friend is a bit young and inexperienced to be riding a pony like that on his own, but they seem to understand each other."

Merrie and Philip attended to Sambo's drink and meal and then went off to have one of their own.

36

Herds of bewildered ponies

CHAPTER VI

THE FOAL AT THE FAIR

JUST as Dartmoor can produce the most dreadful weather imagin-
able, so can it favour us with a day so perfect that the colour,
the clear outlines, the misty distances, the vital air and the sunlight
turn it into an enchanted land.

Such a day dawned for the expedition to Gorsebridge. The
children were vaguely aware of the lovely hills and valleys, followed
by rolling moorland and tors topped by granite as they journeyed
in Davy's dad's truck, but they were more taken up with the thought
of all the ponies they would see.

Davy's dad was Mr. Hurrell and the truck contained a number
of sheep which had to be dropped at a market on the way. Mr.
Hurrell intended to go on to the pony fair, to see what was doing
and perhaps to get a load for the homeward journey.

The fair was in a field on the side of a hill. Other fields led up
and down to the edge of the moor, which seemed to be very silent
in the sunshine, stretching away freely and satisfyingly into space.

Herds of bewildered wild ponies were being driven along the

road and into pens in the field, where they were sorted out one by one, and chased before the auctioneer, who accepted bids before they passed out into another pen. Sometimes it was very hard to see them because of the crowd round the auctioneer, with the pony in its midst.

After wandering round to inspect the "suckers"—this year's foals, many of them to be separated from their mothers for the first time—one or two proud, powerfully-made little stallions, a number of fine young colts and all the rest of the ponies of various ages, the three children clambered on to a bank to eat an early lunch, much needed after a very early breakfast. There were a few odd riding ponies, bigger than the Dartmoors, who would be offered at the end of the sale, but nothing that interested Philip very much.

"Except the stallions, there isn't one I like as well as Sambo," announced Merrie.

"No, he's a good sort of pony," agreed Davy. "Great strong limbs on him. Should jump, most Dartmoors do."

"You know a lot about ponies," said Merrie, who wanted to find out Mayflower's history.

"Should do. They are always coming and going through our yard. Dad often has a load of ponies to rail."

"Have you had Mayflower a long time?"

"Only this spring—in May. I wanted a pony awful bad and Dad 'ould never let me have one. He always said there were plenty passing through and I could pick up a ride here and there.

"Then one day an old gent drove into the yard with a ralli cart and some shining harness and Mayflower stepping out like a champion. But she was in an awful sweat and trembling when she stood still.

"He shouted to Dad to give him a fair price for the trap and harness, but he didn't want anything for the pony. I could see Dad wondering what was up, but he bid him a price. 'Your son can have the pony,' the old boy said, and took the money and cleared out.

" 'Put the pony in the field,' Dad says to me. And I did. She was frightened to death of us. She'd lay back her ears and snap and

kick if we went near her. But I used to go and see her and take her
food every day and she got quite sweet with me."

"Why did you call her Mayflower?"

"Well, there was a May tree in the field and it was awful pretty.
And I guessed she'd had a lot of adventures, like the explorers on
the *Mayflower* ship."

"Did you have any adventures when you first rode her?" asked
Philip.

"Guess I did. I never had no lessons. Dad told me a thing or
two. I pick up a bit at the Pony Club rallies."

"Oh, I am glad you don't know an awful lot," cried Merrie, who
had feared that she would not be up to the standard of the two
boys.

The day wore on and the children wandered about, watching
the ponies, many of whom would have liked to be free again. It
was very tantalizing to see so many change hands and not to bid
for one of them.

At last they were all sold, herded, loaded into lorries for the
station or driven off to their new homes. Merrie, separated from
the two boys, watched the antics of a foal, smaller and younger
than any she had seen, evidently a late foal, careering about from
pen to pen, whinneying madly in the search of its mother.

It was repeatedly chased away, very pretty, very wild and more
and more frightened. She took her courage in both hands and
went to one of the moor men to ask what had happened.

"Reckon there's been a mistake. Reckon it's mother's been
driven off somewhere and that it got into the wrong pen and missed
its load."

The little foal continued its canters, full of life, supple, graceful,
puzzled. It whinnied again, not knowing that its mother was travel-
ling farther and farther from it.

Merrie began to wonder what would happen to it. She might,
however, have left it to its fate but she overheard one of the men
saying it would have to go for meat.

"No," she cried, startling them. "No, you can't. Not that sweet
little thing. I—I want it. I—I'll pay!" And Philip and Davy arrived
as she burst into floods of tears, a very tired and worried little girl.

39

She heard the men advising Philip to take her home, and stopped crying/to explain, finishing up with, "It'll do for Fooze."

"But . . ." began Philip.

"Your parents may not want it," said Mr. Hurrell.

"It's most unusual," said the auctioneer, who, having finished his job and his sandwiches and beer, had now joined the group.

The "buts", the difficulties, and a feeling of utter desperation and of pity for the little dancing, frightened foal, still unaware that it might soon leave the moor for ever, soon cease to exist, drove Merrie to use her wits and to find the answer to problems which would have defeated her earlier in the day.

Somehow she managed to convince these stone-cold lumps of granite, these enemies of youth, of foals, and children, as the men now appeared to her, that the foal would be accepted at her home, even if bought by so small and penniless a girl. That if any claim was made she would give it up (Philip joined in here). And that it would be far simpler to give way and find out how right she was than to go on fighting.

The end of it all was that Philip produced a pound, given to him by his parents to carry in case of emergencies on the journey, and swore that the remaining four pounds or so should be sent (out of their savings) from home. Mr. Hurrell agreed to fit the foal in with his load, and Davy, while all the arrangements were being made, set to work with the moor men to round it up.

Their arrival home, as it began to get dark, with a very small and very hungry Dartmoor pony a few months old was quite spectacular. Foozalum was asleep in bed and could not welcome the new friend destined to grow up with him. Endless explanations had to be made, but these were eased by the children's supreme confidence that they had done the right thing.

Uncle Joe insisted that as their paddock had not been eaten bare, was in a good situation well drained and watered, and skirted by a stream, the little foal was old enough to fend for himself, which he might not have been successful in doing in a parched meadow burnt dry by the summer sun.

Merrie and Philip's mother, Mrs. Lovell, did not know much about horses, but she was rather worried at the idea of a frightened, tiny foal, away from its mother for the first time when only a few months old, and insisted that they should offer it milk in a bucket or a bottle. Their father brought it some bran, which it did not understand and would not eat that night, though it soon grew to like it.

The great moment came when, having refused all their offers, it was carefully introduced to Sambo, who fortunately showed a not unfriendly spirit. Uncle Joe was a little worried because Sambo had shoes on and would have hurt the foal badly had he kicked it. However, they decided to leave it loose in the field with him for company rather than shut it in the stable, or in their little fenced-in manège at the side.

Eventually the children went to bed, leaving Uncle Joe smoking a last pipe and keeping an eye on the two ponies as an early moon rose over the distant hills.

The foal ran round the field whinnying anxiously, but after a while it found its way to the water which was so essential to it. It did not settle immediately, but eventually began to snatch little bits of the refreshing, dew-laden grass, encouraged by Sambo's example and soothed by the pleasant sounds of night-life in the countryside.

After Uncle Joe had made doubly sure there was nowhere it could force its way or even jump out, or anything in which it might get caught up, he stayed near at hand for about an hour, then went to bed feeling pretty sure that all was well.

CHAPTER VII

SOME REAL HARD WORK

THE following morning Uncle Joe announced that this was beyond a joke—time was going by and they had done no real riding practice at all. No, they might not spend the morning introducing Foozalum to the foal. They were going to do some practice in the little "school" he had made in the field. Thus Sambo would remain near enough for the foal to see him and it would not become frightened by being left alone.

When they were all gathered in the field Uncle Joe himself saddled and bridled Sambo once or twice and made them point out some of the things which were wrong. Then he fitted the tack correctly and told Merrie to give them a demonstration of mounting, first of all making sure that the saddle was girthed up sufficiently tightly to prevent it slipping round when she got up.

He explained that it is quite wrong to have the girths too loose as the saddle gets out of place, and bits of gravel, dirt and so forth may get thrown up and lodge between the girth and the skin. Also, too loose a girth may rub backwards and forwards and cause soreness, just as too tight a one is harmful. And it was necessary to see that no skin was pinched between two girths if two were used, or between the end of the saddle flap and the girth.

Merrie gathered the reins in her left hand on Sambo's neck, making sure she did not pull on his mouth, faced his tail, put her left foot in the stirrup and hopped round very neatly with her hand just over the far side of the saddle, and up, without sticking her left toe into his ribs, or touching his back with her right leg as it "went over the top".

Uncle Joe said that some people believed in catching hold of the back of the saddle, which might be necessary with a very high horse or pony, but he did not do it if he could help it because it shifted the saddle on the pony's back.

"Tell us how you are going to sit and why," he asked Merrie.

"So that anyone could put a stick through me and it would be a straight line from my head to my heels," she announced proudly.

"Yes," said Uncle. "Sit nice and straight and *down* into the toes on a line with your knees. You must have the *flat* of your thigh against the saddle, not the back of it, mind. The knees must be close to the saddle, and be bent and pointing the way you want to go. Your elbows fairly close to your body, but not stiff, and your hands down. Now, how do you move off?"

"I shorten my reins if they are loose——"

"How?" broke in Uncle Joe.

"By taking hold of the end of the left-hand rein with my right hand and sliding it through my fingers and the same with the right-hand rein, using my left hand, and always remembering to shorten from behind, never in front. This helps to make Sambo rather collected and alert. I press him with my legs and feel his mouth, and off we go."

"Go on, then," said Uncle Joe.

It all worked beautifully and Merrie practised turning very successfully. When she wanted to go to the left she pressed Sambo with her right leg and felt her left rein. And when she wanted to go to the right she pressed him with her left leg and felt her right rein. Always the opposite hand and leg.

The hand controls the front half or forehand of the pony, the leg his rear half or quarters, and the reason you use the opposite hand and leg is because the pony's quarters must follow the forehand as smoothly as possible and your leg prevents them from flying out in the wrong direction on the turn. A good rider takes care not to move in the saddle or shift this weight about carelessly, as it is possible to turn a well-trained pony by the weight alone and the way it is placed.

Merrie persuaded Sambo to come to a stop by closing both legs (this helps to bring his hocks under him and acts as a brake) and feeling his mouth (not hauling on it), easing the reins the instant he responded.

Having already had several days' practice at this, she set about trotting. Uncle Joe made her hand her reins over Sambo's head

43

to Philip, fold her arms, and practise rising first of all with her stirrups and then without, while Sambo stood still. She was inclined to rise much too high and to come down with a bump when using her stirrups, either of which faults would have been very unfortunate if Sambo had really been trotting, and would have prevented her from getting the time or rhythm. At first she had some difficulty with her stirrups, until she found she must not have her knees too high on the saddle. Once she got the knack it was quite easy, and she learned not to depend on her hands or the reins for balance as sometimes Uncle Joe made her fold her arms, at other times let them hang at her side, and at others again made her clasp her two hands together and let them lie in front of her.

After quite a short while they dropped this exercise, which was intended merely to give her some idea of how to use her muscles deliberately, and of what it felt like to leave the saddle. Then Philip ran beside a slowly trotting Sambo while Merrie bumped the saddle.

This was not very difficult and if she felt unsteady she clutched Sambo's beautiful mane. If he had not had a mane Uncle Joe would have given her a neck strap to seize if necessary. Actually, her few rides on other children's ponies and on Sambo, since his arrival, had given her the feel of her pony and she did not have much trouble in learning to sit the trot.

They practised alternate walks and trots and no attempt was made to "post" or rise until Merrie did not bump too heartily and managed to maintain some sort of position with hands and heels down and knees close to the saddle.

Just as Uncle Joe was going to tell her how good she would probably be the next day and not to spoil it all by overdoing it that day, but to finish off with some quiet walking and turning exercises, a small figure appeared at the gate leading Mayflower.

"Come in, come in," called Uncle Joe, and Davy Hurrell opened the gate and strolled up to them, shooing away the foal, who arrived to inspect Mayflower.

Davy smiled sweetly upon them and came straight to the point, looking at Philip. "You haven't got a pony yet, and you know a

44

The bridle on this pony is crooked, browband too near eyes, throat lash carelessly fastened, bit too high in mouth, strap-ends not through loops (these could easily come undone, besides looking untidy), curb chain fastened over reins. Saddle too far back, girth twisted, stirrup iron swinging at end of leather (can catch in anything, including pony's teeth if he snaps at a fly), buckle half way down instead of at top, loop of leather likely to slip off bar. Pony held incorrectly by front of noseband.

Pony standing comfortably, correctly bridled, saddled and held. Reins secured neatly in position by stirrup irons. Girths flat, and far forward enough (though not too much) to hold saddle in proper place.

Rider in bad position on back of saddle, knees, calf of leg and heel too far forward (should not be in front of girth). Wrists too straight, fingers loose, reins uneven and held incorrectly. Pony half asleep.

What a difference! Pony alert and standing straight. Rider's back is straight but not stiff, might be leaning a shade more forward from waist, and heel a little further back so that point of toe is in line with knee. Foot nicely in centre of stirrup with slight pressure on inside—this automatically closes the knee against the saddle. Little finger through reins, which come out between thumb and first finger.

bit. Thought you and Mayflower could have a nice school together if your uncle's agreeable."

Philip flushed with pleasure and murmured, "Thank you."

"God bless my soul, a grand idea," declared Uncle Joe. "Particularly as we don't know what the pony can do. And you'll have to join us, my boy. We can probably help you a bit, too."

The fascinated Merrie left her walks, turns and finishing exercises, I am sorry to say, to join the little group. There was quite a to-do in making Philip acquainted with Mayflower—who was clearly not a lady likely to suffer liberties from strange riders in whom she had no confidence—and getting mounted and properly settled in the saddle with the stirrups the right length.

Actually the stirrup irons which were too big for Davy were not too big for Philip and Uncle Joe made him alter the length when he was in the saddle, with his arm through the reins, which he pointed out must not be left lying loose on Mayflower's neck, and which would easily be lost were she to put her head down to eat grass, or start off unexpectedly.

Philip kept his foot in the iron to steady it (and to be prepared should anything make the pony play up), taking hold of the strap with his right hand, and gradually releasing it until the tongue slid into what he thought was the right hole. He took care to see that the stirrups were a level length each side, to press the buckle back into the right position against the bar under the flap, to make sure it was not pulled half off the bar, and to fold the end of the strap back under the hanging leather, *not* to thread it through the buckle. This sounds as if it took a long time, but once it becomes a habit it can be done very quickly and almost without thinking.

Mayflower had stood remarkably patiently throughout all this, with Davy at her head, offering an occasional soothing pat and watching the proceedings with interest. As soon as he was ready, Philip spoke to her, shortened his reins and established a gentle, a very gentle contact and closed his legs. Had he kicked her, a lady with Mayflower's temperament would have probably sprung into a gallop, and thrown in a bounce or two for full measure.

As it was, she walked away alert and tranquil and after once or twice round the field to gain her confidence Philip pressed her into

45

a trot with great success. She seemed anxious to trot fast, to scamper along, but he maintained a gentle, steady contact with her mouth, his hands still, and this kept her at a sensible pace.

Uncle Joe was very pleased to see how easily he rode her and how steady and light his hands were. Remembering what had taken place at the Pony Club rally he called him over. "Very good, my boy," he said. "No faults to find. But we don't want to upset the little mare by taking any chances at the canter. Bring her into our manège first, and remember two things—*never* go into a canter from a fast trot and never throw the reins to her and send her on in a haphazard way, or you'll lose control."

In the manège, Philip asked Mayflower to canter by the closing of his legs, and a slight feel of her mouth, his own body giving imperceptible forward impulse. She broke immediately and readily into the canter from a nice ordinary trot, and Philip managed to keep her very nicely balanced between his hands and his legs. Never once having let her get out of control, he had no difficulty whatever in keeping her where he wanted her. Things might have been different if she had once gained the upper hand or if he had been afraid of her.

"Heigh!" called Uncle Joe. "You're doing jolly well. We'll just do one or two circles and then Davy shall have a go." He strolled into the middle of the manège. "Now I am going to be the centre of your circle until you get the hang of it or else we shall have you doing all sorts of extraordinary shapes instead of circles. You must keep ten yards away from me all the time. Sit upright, don't slouch and to keep Mayflower going smoothly *round* instead of straight you'll have to use your hands and legs—good practice for you both."

Philip set off at a walk and soon found out how true were these words. He had to use both legs very gently to keep a somewhat bored Mayflower up to her bridle (this term is sometimes used more emphatically in dressage or training and is then called "on the bit"), and when necessary a gentle pressure of the right leg kept her going round in the circle and the left leg prevented her from turning in too much.

However, he did not have to use his legs a great deal except to

46

keep her up into the bridle ("to help provide the correct impulsion" is another way of putting it). Somewhat to his surprise, he found he had to keep more contact with his outside rein than he expected. But it was only by gentle incessant use of hand and leg in unison that he completed his good circle. He rode with a fairly long—but not loose—rein, sitting erect but not stiff.

"Let me give you a tip before you start to trot, Philip," called Uncle Joe. "Keep your eyes looking in front of you, ahead of your pony, in the direction in which you aim to go, and you'll find that Mayflower will go that way much more easily."

Philip got Mayflower at a quiet, steady trot, no sharp increases or decreases of speed, and this magic formula worked amazingly well.

Davy, who was watching his pony silently and intently, was much interested in this and inquired: "Why does it help?"

"Well, I really don't know, my boy, except that if you want to walk on a straight line across a narrow plank bridge you'll do much better if you look straight ahead of you, not at your toes or the bit of ground just in front. You get a much better sense of direction and determination to get there and your balance is better, all of which affects your pony. Exactly the same thing applies if you want to ride a straight line instead of a circle."

Merrie arrived and said she wanted to walk a circle with Sambo, which she did rather waveringly, aided by one or two gentle kicks instead of leg pressure only.

In the meanwhile the energetic Davy had vaulted on to Mayflower's back and trotted gaily off to the top of the field, where he turned her and cantered her back and past the other ponies. Uncle Joe insisted that he must canter past so that the little mare should never get the habit of dashing up to and stopping near any group of ponies.

Not yet quite as smooth in his orders to his pony as Philip, he did it very well and remarked that it was very easy when you knew how. This caused Uncle Joe to smile and threaten him with much more difficult ponies which he would never be able to ride unles he practised hard. "Want a bit of thrill, do you?" he inquired finally.

"Can I have a jump?" asked Davy, who had spotted some poles.

"Not to-day," said Uncle Joe. "But we'll have a real good go at it one day. And I'm going to study the Pony Club tests so that we can work for them. Now we'll finish up with some exercises for you all."

The exercises will be found in the Appendix, on pages 115 and 116, and all three children carried them out fairly neatly as they were quite amusing and exciting.

It is most important to have a "strong" seat, and these exercises help to make riders supple, fit and well-balanced. Some people make a bad mistake by thinking that if they have good hands there is really very little else to worry about. Not only does a strong seat make it possible to use the hands correctly, but without it no one can get beyond a certain standard.

When the seat is correct the rider is always much happier and freer. Just as a pony is schooled to use his forehand and quarters equally well, so must the rider be in full command of his or her seat, thighs, legs and hands—impossible if he or she is in the wrong position.

CHAPTER VIII

ANOTHER PONY, PLEASE

Two ponies among three children—oh yes, it is true enough that they were very lucky to have them, especially as there was Foozle's little foal to play with into the bargain. She had become quite friendly and Foozle adored her, staggering after her with every tempting titbit he could think of, from a bunch of lettuce leaves to a piece of toffee.

But time was getting on and Philip ached to have his own pony before term started. The Wideawake's boy's hunter, Rowan, which he had seen at the Pony Club rally, seemed as unattainable as ever, and although they had been to look at two children's hunters which had been advertised, both ran well into three figures and Uncle Joe had said a regretful "no".

Davy arrived one morning with the information, gleaned goodness knows how, that Rowan would be sold for £500, and that his breeding involved a thorough-bred polo pony sire and an Exmoor mare, but exactly where they appeared in the pedigree he did not know.

Philip knew only too well that it was useless to go on thinking of Rowan, or to dream of making a trip to Ireland and finding exactly the right animal in a boreen on the side of a mountain.

Davy, however, was away on another line.

"Never mind about Rowan *now*," said he. "Dad says there's a useful pony in the valley. Not much to look at but likely to do a useful job of work, and won't cost the earth."

So they all bundled once again into the "Beetle" and set off to see the pony in the valley, which belonged to one of Mr. Hurrell's farmer friends. Just as Davy had said, he wasn't much to look at, was "ordinary", not much quality or breeding about him, yet he was a well-put-together pony, hard to fault.

The two boys looked in his mouth, noticed that the middle four front teeth in his lower jaw were permanent ones with a slight hollowness in the centre, known as "the mark", but that he still had his two outside milk teeth, and declared him to be four years old.

"I like him," said Philip. "He's a nice height——"

"Likely to do you for several years," put in Uncle Joe. Actually the pony stood about fourteen hands one inch.

"He'll live in or out and do any kind of job," said his owner.

"Good set of legs, fairly low to the ground, not 'on the leg' at all," contributed Davy's father, who had appeared from nowhere.

"He's nice and short and strong," said Merrie, not to be left out.

"You mean compact," corrected Uncle Joe. "Anyway, up you get, Philip, and have a ride."

Philip had not ridden many young, green ponies in his life, and did not realize that it meant that his present mount was very uneducated and behind his bridle, when he wavered about and did not understand what was asked of him, but he was quick to sense the pony's willingness and easy movement, and jumped down better satisfied than ever.

"Well, we're taking a chance on a young, untrained pony, and we don't know how he'll turn out—but how much do you want for him?" asked Uncle Joe when he had examined him carefully and found no blemish or weakness.

Eventually the pony became Philip's for fifty pounds, and to his great joy he was allowed to borrow a saddle and bridle and ride him the eight miles home.

It was an interesting ride, as although some of it lay along the roads and lanes, quite a lot was across country, and he had never before been so far alone.

Uncle Joe found out that the pony, who by now had somehow acquired the name of Alex, after the two generals of modern and of ancient times, both of whom were held in veneration by Philip, was not nervous of traffic. But all the same he advised Philip to keep out of the way of it and of all unusual-looking things, with so young and unschooled an animal.

They followed quietly behind him with the "Beetle" for the first half-mile, then hurried home to prepare for his arrival. Merrie in particular was anxious to tell Sambo, Foozle and the foal (now Twinkle by name) about their beautiful new brother, who was a liver-chestnut with a lovely dark tail, but alas! no mane.

Davy, who was always very practical in his plans, rushed home to get his Mayflower and go and meet them. He rode back in the direction of the valley farm with his handy little ride-and-drive

Alex galloped past him, stirrups flying, head in the air

pony, singing and whistling to himself, and taking a short cut which led him right across the line of country which he expected Philip to be following. You can imagine his horror when Alex galloped past him, stirrups flying, head in the air.

For a moment Davy could not make up his mind what to do, whether first to go in search of Philip or to catch the pony. He decided that Philip was probably all right and it would be much more useful to take the pony with him if he could catch him without much delay.

So he followed quietly after Alex, knowing full well that if he galloped Alex would merely run away the faster and Mayflower might get excited and out of control, reducing the whole thing to a race between the two.

To his delight Davy saw Alex canter through an open gate into a particularly luscious looking field. He allowed him to settle down to eating grass, then sidled up to him, taking great care not to startle him with a sudden movement, and was lucky enough to get the reins, which had fallen over his head and were lying on the ground. He ran the stirrups up and set off back with the two ponies, to be met before long by a very shame-faced Philip, who climbed into the saddle and told him the story as they rode along together.

"Alex was as good as gold," said Philip. "We walked along the road and cantered over the bit of downland and I decided I'd take a short cut through the woods. There was a pole across the path to stop cattle from going in, but it was only a very low one, and I thought 'I'll see if I can jump it'.

"Sounds easy enough, but honestly you never saw anything like the way Alex took off! I thought he was going to hit the sky, and I just went for six! I was winded and couldn't do much for a minute or two, by which time he was gone. And was I worried for fear anything should happen to him."

Davy looked mildly gratified as if he and his father had helped to find a champion. "Dad reckoned he could jump," he said. "That's why he wanted you to have him."

The whole story was repeated at length to the eagerly waiting family. Uncle Joe was not altogether approving. "Glad you didn't hurt yourself. Glad he's such a good natural jumper," he said. "But to go and jump a new young pony the first time you ride him, when you've never jumped before, is a bit silly. However, no harm done."

A good way of leading a pony. These two are standing side by side—one is not dragging behind the other. The rider is holding the snaffle reins, the curb reins having been slipped back over the saddle.

Rider should have his weight on his stirrups a little more, his knee to the saddle and not be sitting down quite so much. If he had kept his heel down and the weight on the inside of the stirrup as he approached the jump the position might have been better.

Rider's position excellent. He has got his pony going well into his bridle and is just coming round a slight bend before turning in for the jump.

CHAPTER IX

HOW DO THEY JUMP?

"No," said Uncle Joe the following morning. "No, *no* and *no!*"

It did not sound a very propitious opening to the day, did it?—but his next words explained what he meant.

"I know perfectly well—you've told me enough times—that Alex seems to be a natural jumper and that you think he will win us all a fortune in the show ring so that we can buy Rowan, but Alex won't even be fully grown and developed until he is five, and he's got to be *educated* before he takes to show jumping. So have you!

"What? Start to learn together to-day? Not likely. If you are so mad to learn to jump now, you shall have some jumping on Sambo perhaps, but you've got other jobs to do to-day. You and Alex must start your education, Merrie must do a bit of real work, and I want to see if you two have any idea of tack cleaning."

I am sorry to say that Merrie made a face at this, calling down Uncle Joe's wrath upon her head. He went to some trouble to point out that life was not one long round of pleasure, and that if they wanted to enjoy the Pony Club they must pass the Tests, which included the care of saddlery, stable management and goodness knows what.

He rounded it off in style by saying he had collected together quite a lot of tack, the use of which he wanted to explain.

They hurried off to the field, where Merrie had an hour's practice, beginning with physical exercises on Sambo's patient back (if Sambo had not been at grass and able to keep himself exercised, they would have had to ride him for about half an hour or so, before expecting him to stand still).

She practised mounting and dismounting, shortening and lengthening her reins without jerking his mouth even slightly, some of the exercises described in the appendix to the last chapter, walking and trotting as well as circling, turning, stopping and starting at the walk.

Philip had been busy photographing Foozle and Twinkle lying on the ground together. He had also been trying to convince Alex that there was no need for him to have any objection to being caught. To impress upon his mind the advantages of surrender he allowed him to eat more oats out of the bucket than was really wise.

Alex was groomed, saddled and bridled and ready for work just about the time Uncle Joe finished with Merrie and Sambo, and it was a proud boy who rode him into the practice ring.

He looked about him a good deal, and, as was the case on the preceding day, he did not go up to his bit. However, Uncle Joe told Philip to walk him about on a loose rein for ten minutes.

At the end of that time he took him back into the main paddock and made him walk and trot in turns, first in one direction for as far as he could within the confines of the field, and then in another. Philip pressed him on with the legs and persuaded him to stretch out his neck and the muscles of his back as much as possible.

At the end of half an hour Alex and Philip returned to the ring to practise a few big circles first to one rein (or side) and then to another, but never going round in the same direction for too long.

Uncle Joe watched with an eagle eye to see that Philip used the aids (the hand and the leg) correctly, and without any roughness or exaggeration. He also insisted that they should keep to the same pace or time in the trot as far as possible. They were allowed a short canter to finish up with, at the end of what was, in all, an hour's ride.

When they had finished Uncle Joe called the children together for a little talk. "No doubt you have been wondering what we've been driving at," he said. "Well, this four-year-old pony of Philip's has been quite passably broken in, is used to the bridle and saddle, but he doesn't yet know how to *use* himself properly, nor has he ever been taught to understand the rider's wishes or orders quickly and easily. That takes time.

"Philip wants his pony to take him riding across the country, to Pony Club rallies, perhaps a bit of hunting in the winter and perhaps a bit of show jumping next year. He doesn't want to train him for High School, but he does want to get the best out of him for everyday needs and that as quickly as possible.

"Well, before we *can* teach a young pony very much we've got to get him going freely forward with a rider on his back. Remember all his movements when a colt has been without a weight on his back, or any interference with his head and mouth.

"We've got to get him to extend himself a bit, to stretch his back and neck, to stride out as far as he can, to *use* himself to the fullest extent, before we think about collecting and balancing him and making him attentive to our needs.

"That's why I've been getting Philip to maintain only the very lightest contact with Alex's mouth, just enough to give him confidence and no more, and to drive him on (but not too emphatic a drive) to stretch and move and use himself. He should do it all himself if possible—help him, yes; force him, no.

"Bit by bit we'll get him doing all we want and fairly quickly we'll make a useful pony of him, with a thorough grounding, but first he's got to do plenty of what I call free, liberty work and work across country, as well as in the ring."

The children found this new line of thought interesting. So did Davy who had appeared with Mayflower to ask if they could try a jump.

"Really you children do set me problems," declared Uncle Joe. "You've never jumped, and you don't know whether Mayflower has? Well, as far as I can see, the best thing is to call on Sambo, who is the most sensible of you all."

Uncle Joe had been going to make a small lane of low jumps over which they could practise, but owing to their impatience this was not yet ready. However, he had several poles and some nice cross-pieces of wood to stand them on.

He placed one of these poles on its cross-pieces at the side of the little manège. It stood just over a foot high.

"Now, you are really very lucky as you've nothing to worry about," Uncle Joe said to Philip, as he watched him vault on to the waiting Sambo. "You've got a willing, sensible pony who knows the job and you can leave everything to him for the first time or two.

"All you've got to do is to start off in the right position, take great care not to get rigid as you approach the jump, and let yourself be swung over with Sambo. You'll have no reins, as I'm not risking a jab on his mouth, and you can grab his mane or have a neck strap if you don't feel comfortable."

The photograph facing page 53 explains how Philip followed Uncle Joe's advice, and got his body into the correct position to start with. He then cantered quietly round half the ring with the knotted reins lying on the neck of the obedient Sambo. He took care to press on his irons and negotiated the small jumps so easily that Uncle Joe made him practise with folded arms once or twice, and also without his stirrups. Eventually he was sent over two poles one after the other—they stood about fifteen feet apart. He was only allowed in all about a dozen attempts at the jumps that morning.

I may add that he worked hard at his jumping through the rest of the holidays, realizing more and more the importance of getting his weight well poised on his knees and feet so that he might swing over the obstacles with the pony with the minimum of movement in the lower part of his body. He gradually learnt the different feel of the spread and the upright jumps, and how to keep his contact with the pony's mouth without in any way interfering with its balance while in the air or landing.

But the problem of Mayflower still remained, and it was finally decided to run up the stirrups, fix the reins loosely to the saddle and send her over poles without a rider for the first time.

Mayflower, I am sorry to say, came tearing up to the first jump as if she were demented and then stopped dead. Had Davy been on her back she would probably have shot him a considerable distance. On being asked to reconsider her decision, Mayflower, still at top speed, jumped all three superbly, finishing off with a couple of really natty bucks just to show how she had enjoyed it.

Uncle Joe said she was a lady with a past and he'd like to know what it was. He also said that Davy would have to start jumping on Sambo, but he thought both Sambo and himself had had quite enough for one morning and they would now have a nice restful time looking at all the saddlery he'd laid out for them to inspect—and cleaning some of it.

CHAPTER X

SADDLES AND BRIDLES

THE saddlery collected at some pains by Uncle Joe and laid out for the children's inspection consisted of the following things:

(1) A bridle, or head-piece attached to an ordinary plain snaffle. Beside it lay a twisted, an egg-butt, a chain, and a rubber snaffle; a vulcanite Pelham bit, a half-moon Pelham made of steel, not vulcanite; an ordinary double bit with a sliding mouth-piece; a very thin-looking but much more severe one with a higher port and a fixed bar. Beside them lay a dropped noseband.

(2) A running martingale, a standing martingale, a pair of Irish rings and an old-fashioned breast-plate.

(3) Three saddles, one of which was a side-saddle. A folded leather girth, a string girth, a twisted leather girth, and a canvas or web girth.

(4) A day rug, a night rug, a sheet and two surcingles.

These made quite an impressive showing and all four got chairs and sat down while Uncle Joe talked about them.

"You know what a plain snaffle is," said he, picking it up. "By looking at it you can see how the nutcracker action caused by the joint in the middle affects the pony's jaw. And how it must not be too high or low in the mouth if you want it to act properly, but lying on the toothless bars of his mouth just below the corners of his lips—no wrinkling. Nor must it be so wide that the rings to which the reins are attached are half-way up his jaw bone, or so narrow that they pinch his mouth. You should never put a very thin, light snaffle in your pony's mouth. You will hurt him if you do, as it has a cutting effect. Nor too thick and clumsy a one.

"Now take a look at the twisted snaffle, quite solid and heavy—

57

actually they vary a lot according to what you want—and with these sinister ridges which give it the name of 'twisted'. This is a very powerful bit and affects the bars of the pony's mouth and his tongue, but should not worry him if used by someone with light hands, and treated respectfully.

"This egg-butt snaffle is much the same as a plain snaffle, but has this straight piece in the ring which is supposed to bring the pressure to bear more evenly—it happens to suit some horses better.

"Now we come to a real difference, as neither the chain snaffle nor the rubber snaffle are jointed. You probably won't see much of the chain snaffle, which looks more like a curb chain than a bit, as it is mostly used in breaking—the youngsters like the feel of it better than the heavier jointed snaffle, and will play with it. This helps to keep their mouth wet, which is so important, as a dry-mouthed pony is often a hard-mouthed pony, and they will give to it and perhaps bend their heads and flex their jaw a little. The rubber snaffle will often please a pony with a light or else difficult mouth, and he will go well in it when he is hard to manage in anything else.

"Now before looking at any of the other bits we'd better consider the double, as I suppose the snaffle and the double bridle are really the basis of all the rest.

"The snaffle we know about, but you will see here that when the pony has to learn to accept two bits in his mouth the snaffle is lighter than when it is the one and only bit and has all the pressure on it. It is now called the snaffle or bridoon, and that which goes with it, its other half, so to speak, is called the curb or bit.

"Now take a good look at this particular one I am showing you. The bars at either side are not too long, or they would have too powerful, perhaps painful, a leverage, and the bar across the middle —across the pony's mouth—is raised a little in the centre. This part is called the port and lies against the tongue very comfortably —or should do. A very big or high port is sometimes used on a pulling pony, as it is very powerful, but it is not to be recommended as a rule.

"Now this mouth-piece with the port in it is not fixed where it

58

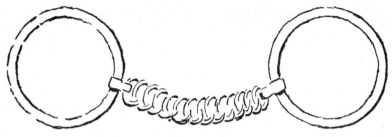

Chain snaffle

joins the two outside bars, so that it can slide up and down a little way if the pony moves his jaw or his tongue. These two bits, the snaffle or bridoon and the curb or bit, must lie comfortably in the pony's mouth, with the snaffle on top and neither pinching nor wrinkling his lips. They are each attached to the head-piece by a separate strap.

"Some people like them sewn on to the head-piece, some buckled. Those sewn on look a little neater, but sewing prevents either head-piece or bit from being inter-changeable with other ones.

"Of the two reins used, one attached to the snaffle or bridoon and the other to the curb or bit, the thicker or wider should be attached to the snaffle, and the narrower one to the curb.

"Before going on to the next lot, I'd like to see if you realize how the double bridle works. You tell us something, Davy."

Davy had never thought very seriously about it, but he knew how to look for a reason, and his imagination was quickly at work.

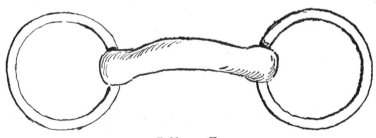

Rubber snaffle

59

"Well," said he slowly, and thinking hard, "you've got two bits to use and they can hardly work exactly the same. And with the reins attached to the bottom of these two cheek pieces there's a big pull on the bit which must bring the pony's head in."

"How right you are!" said Uncle Joe. "Actually the action of the snaffle *helps* to raise the head, and the curb to lower it or bring it in. And if you've got a good, secure seat and know how to use your hands aright, you can tell your pony so much with the use of those two bits that he is able to obey you twice as easily. The double bridle isn't meant as a double brake, and to look upon it like that will probably mean a spoilt pony."

"You've forgotten something," said Merrie, very pleased with herself.

"And so I have—the curb-chain!" said Uncle Joe. "Very important, too. Not just as a drag. Not just to tighten against the pony's jaw, hurt him and leave a permanent mark, but to hold the curb or bit in place.

"Some people use leather or part-elastic curb chains. If you use a steel one you *must* unravel all the links and have it lying flat in the groove of your pony's jaw, or else the edge of a twisted link will cut against the flesh and madden him if you pull the curb rein. It should not be hanging so loose that it bounces up and down, but it should give plenty of play to the curb bit. You can test it by moving the cheek pieces of the bit backwards, and making sure the chain does not then press too tightly against your pony's jaw bone.

"The little link in the middle of the chain should be in the middle of the back of his mouth. On some bits there is a curb-strap to hold it in place, which is a very good thing."

Philip, who had been examining the second double bridle, wanted to know what was the reason for the difference.

"It's only a little light bit, and I expect it is for ponies with very light mouths," Merrie suggested.

"That's just where you are wrong, and why I brought it along to-day," declared Uncle Joe. "I hope you won't ever need to use this type of bit, but you'll probably see it on some ponies and wonder what it is.

An exercise—trotting with arms held straight above the head.

Practising jumping. All three ponies are rising well at the hedge, and the riders have good positions in the saddle and an excellent contact with the ponies' mouths, but no sign of interference or discomfort.

A double bridle, i.e., snaffle or bridoon and curb or bit, plus curb chain. The snaffle is jointed in the middle, the bit has a slight arch in the centre known as a port, and it is not fixed but moves up and down where it joins the bar at the side. These are just a nice length, not too long or severe. The curb chain is attached to hooks at the side and must always be flat as shown in this picture.

There are two nice saddles here. You can see they are raised in front and behind, and there is an air passage down the centre. The stirrups hang from the bars at the side and it will be seen that the safety catch is down, which makes the bars look rather long. The pommel is the front arch, the cantle the rear arch and the seat is in the middle.

"This thin-looking bit has a sharp, cutting effect, the long cheek piece at each side provides lots of leverage and so makes it even more severe, and look, the mouth-piece is fixed at the sides so that it cannot slide comfortably about—there is no give and take if the pony moves his tongue or jaw under it—and the high port covers more of his tongue, thereby having quite a severe action.

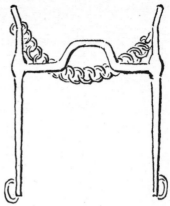

Severe bit with high port, fixed bar and long cheek

"I have seen this kind of double bit used effectively on a pony whose mouth has been ruined by bad riding, and I have seen it used by a child who had very little strength but naturally light hands. I think it is a dangerous bit to give such a child. It is certainly one that can very easily madden a pony which it does not suit."

Davy picked up the two bits and compared them—the ordinary double of moderate, comfortable thickness, with shortish cheek pieces, a low port and a sliding mouth-piece (which he saw fit to term as "champable"), and the much lighter, thinner bit with long cheek pieces, high port and fixed mouth-piece.

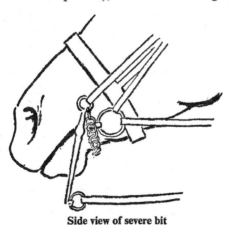

Side view of severe bit

In the meanwhile Uncle Joe had turned his attention to the two Pelhams, one of vulcanite and one of plain steel. Two pairs of reins are used with a Pelham, just as they are with a double, but there is only one bit instead of two. This consists of a single mouth-piece attached to two bars with a ring for the reins at the top and the bottom.

61

Uncle Joe explained that the mouth-piece could be sliding or fixed, and either straight or half-moon shape. On this occasion the vulcanite bar was straight but not fixed. It was quite light and pleasant to the touch, but very much thicker than the steel one, which was about as thick as an ordinary light plain snaffle, and was half-moon shape. Some ponies go better in one, some in another. There was no port, and no joint.

Uncle Joe said that there was quite a lot of disagreement about this bit, which was at least a fairly comfortable one for a pony, and was less likely to cause harm than many others if the rider was careless with his or her hands. He personally preferred what he called the basic bits, the snaffle and the short double, but was willing to concede that sometimes the Pelham suited both pony and rider best.

All three children pounced on the dropped noseband with interest, having seen some of the famous jumpers wearing it. How it looks and how it is fitted is shown in the diagram. Uncle Joe explained that it was worn with a snaffle and that the idea was that it worked in conjunction with the snaffle as a sort of second string without bringing too much pressure to bear on it. This was why it was used so much in training young horses, as they learnt to understand the rider's signals to their mouth and to obey without too much force or pressure on the bars of the mouth being necessary. Its chief object was to keep the horse's mouth shut, and when fitting the dropped noseband care had always to be taken that it was not too low on his nose and that it did not interfere with his breathing in any way whatever.

Davy here showed signs of special interest, and Uncle Joe gave a laugh and said: "No, boy. You cannot ride your little Mayflower in a dropped noseband. Learn to ride properly and you'll find there's not the slightest need in her case. To let you use it to save yourself trouble wouldn't help you.

"Now we come to the martingales, about which no-one ever seems to agree. What are martingales for?"

"To keep a pony's head down," said Merrie.

"To keep him from getting it up," declared Philip.

"To give you more control," contributed Davy.

"Well, you are all on the right lines, but you've none of you produced the real answer," said Uncle Joe. "The Army explanation is that the martingale is meant to prevent a pony from throwing its head higher than the angle at which it should naturally and properly carry it, and at which you can control it. If it throws its head too high

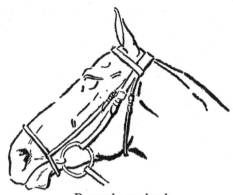

Dropped nose band

the bit cannot act on the bars of the mouth, and it is unbalanced into the bargain. The martingale is not intended to tie a pony's head down, but to act as a preventive if it tries to throw it *too* high, and, as Philip says, to help you to keep him straight—to make it easier for you to ride him properly, and that's the way you want to look at it."

"Well, it doesn't look like that with some of the jumping ponies," announced Davy.

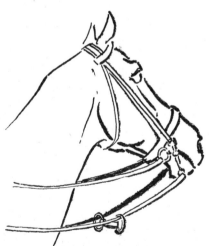

Irish martingale. Note that the throat lash is just right—not too tight or too loose

"No," agreed Uncle Joe. "Over-excitability, bad riding, bad schooling and even a form of fear have brought some of them to such a pass that, rightly or wrongly, their heads now have to be literally tied down. The riders reckon they cannot control them, or that they will get their heads too high to be able to see the jump properly, or—most important of all—they won't be able to arch their backs as they go over if they try and jump with their heads up.

"Anyway let's get back to these three martingales. The first is the running martingale, with rings through which the reins are passed. You must be careful with these rings if you are using a double bridle, as if they are fairly big it is quite possible for them to get caught on the ring of the curb and drive the pony mad with fright. That is why reins often have 'stops' of bone or leather on them—they are easily cut out of a bit of leather. The buckle of the neck strap of the martingale should be on the left side of the neck.

"Some people like the martingale to be attached to the curb rein and some to the snaffle, and they will argue for hours about it, one saying that as the snaffle raises the horse's head it is illogical to use it with the martingale, which prevents it from going above a certain height, others declaring that it is ridiculous to put it on the curb rein, as it produces a wrong pressure. There are other reasons, too. I'm on both sides! I think it depends on the horse and on the rider—anyway I don't like to see it used at all if it can be avoided.

"Here is the standing martingale, which is attached to the nose-band by one single piece of leather, allowing less play than the running martingale, which is divided into two, but suiting some horses best.

"With regard to the right length for both the running and the standing martingales, you can form a rough idea by putting either of them correctly attached to the girth, passing the ends between the animal's front legs, and bringing them up via his chest and the side of his shoulder until the ends just about reach his withers.

"Now these two funny little rings attached to one another by a piece of leather, and which look rather like spectacles, constitute an Irish martingale. They are generally used with a snaffle bridle just to keep the reins from flapping about if a horse throws his head up and down—of course they cannot hold it in place at all, that is for the rider to do. But they do help to keep him straight.

"You don't often see an old-fashioned breast-plate like this nowadays. It was used to 'dress' a horse a bit, and to keep the saddle from slipping back on a narrow-girthed animal. Very useful to hold on by!"

Davy, who seldom missed much, was turning the saddles over and inspecting them.

"Yes," said Uncle Joe. "Quite different, aren't they? I wish I could have got hold of a little, amazingly light racing saddle with its forward flaps to show you, but we'll have to make do with these.

"The first is an ordinary English hunting and showing saddle with fairly straight flaps, so that you can see what kind of a shoulder the show horse has. The other is what used to be looked on as a Continental-type saddle, but is now much more used over here for jumping, and ordinary riding too.

Standing martingale

"You may notice that this second saddle is what we call cut back, at the top end of the pommel, near the withers, the idea being that it shall fit each side of the withers but not run the risk of pressing on them.

"This saddle has a forward flap with some padding under it, to help keep your knees comfortable and in position, and a deep seat. If you were upon it you would feel you were sitting right down into the horse and that nothing could dislodge you! It also has, as all Continental saddles do, a wonderful wide air pas-

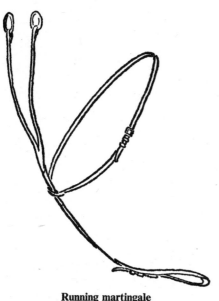

Running martingale

65

sage down the horse's spine—it would be practically impossible for it to press on the spine. Lots of people may prefer the English hunting saddle but the Continental saddle will usually fit a larger number of different animals remarkably well.

"Both are leather-lined, which makes them much easier to clean.

Standing martingale fixed to cavasson noseband. When the horse's nose is raised to the level of the withers the martingale should be just about taut

You see, first of all there is, the iron tree, which is the skeleton of the saddle, then the seat is stretched across it, and the flaps and pommel added. There is lots of padding under it, or it could never be used, and the padding or stuffing is either covered with leather, or serge or linen and must be kept clean.

"Take a look at this modern child's side-saddle, which is very much smaller than the ones children used to use in my young days. A very long time ago only one pommel was used, and then the second one facing in the other direction and called the 'leaping head' was added. Now do you know I think we've done enough for this morning. Go off and get washed for lunch, all of you, and this afternoon we'll put the side-saddle on one of the ponies, and see how it likes it."

"Can I get on?" asked Merrie, thrilled.

"It depends—we'll see," said Uncle Joe, and off they all went to lunch, during which he told them many stories of high-spirited blood-hunters who had been successfully ridden by ladies, chiefly because they felt so secure in their side-saddles that their hands had been light. Sometimes these horses had proved unmanageable when ridden by men.

"*I* think the women would have done just as well astride, but I s'pose no one thought of that, as all ladies rode side-saddle years ago," declared Merrie, firmly.

"Did you ever school a horse to a side-saddle?" inquired Philip of Uncle Joe.

"Yes," replied his long-suffering uncle with a smile. "And I got on so well I thought I'd pop the horse—he was only a youngster—over a fence. Blow me if he didn't turn uncommonly sharp left on landing, and over I went to the right. It was a shocking affair and taught me to be a bit more on the alert, as it need never have happened."

CHAPTER XI

OPERATION SIDE-SADDLE

SAMBO, having worked the hardest of any of the ponies during the morning, took a somewhat poor view of the afternoon programme. However, he was very fond of Merrie, and in addition to this fondness he associated her with nice things, as when she went to catch him she usually produced a small treat, like a bit of apple or carrot or sugar or bread. Or even sometimes a few oats, although oats were strictly and absolutely forbidden as part of a meal.

In view of all this, he allowed himself to be fetched slowly and without much enthusiasm from under the shady trees where he was having an afternoon doze. So did Alexander, who was younger and always on the look-out for something new, and Mayflower, who had been enjoying a bucket of water and a net of hay in the stable. Had it been a very hot day, it is probable that all three ponies would have been kept in the stable until the cool of the evening.

Uncle Joe inquired whether they imagined that the same side-saddle would fit three different-sized ponies, not to mention the little girl rider into the bargain? As all the children wanted to see how their pony went in a side-saddle, this point could only be solved by experiment.

Unfortunately it was too big for Sambo who, however, managed to give the impression that he would look very dashing in one which was made to fit.

It was then gently placed on Mayflower's back and fitted her quite well. There was no question of the unpadded parts coming down on her spine or flesh anywhere, nor did it come rather far forward and interfere with the free action of her shoulders—sometimes the girths will have this effect.

But for all that she did not look very nice in it, as, probably owing to a dash of Hackney blood somewhere, she was just a shade short on her neck, and it looked as if the rider would not have much pony in front of her, despite the fact that Mayflower carried her little head very proudly and well. So, without bothering to do up the girths, the side-saddle was transferred to Alexander.

"Not the side-saddle show pony, perhaps," declared Uncle Joe. "Not quite enough quality. But he'll do very well for me. Now, first of all, we'll do up the under-girth, let him stand for a minute or two, and then tighten it a little bit more, since we mustn't take any chances of letting the side-saddle slide round. Not that there's any need to make it ridiculously tight.

"Then we do the outside strap, and then the balance strap, which goes a little further back round the pony's tummy and of which one end is attached more towards the back of the saddle.

"The idea of the balance strap is just to keep some of the bigger and more old-fashioned saddles from slipping about, just to help steady them. But it is not so necessary with these smaller saddles and is often not used at all. However, I think you should know something about it, as otherwise you may get some surprises."

"I know why," said Davy, looking mysterious, and riveting the attention of Philip and Merrie.

"Tell us, then," from Uncle Joe.

"Well, Dad always said that if you did up a strap too tight round the back part of a horse's tummy, or if his rug and roller worked back, he'd kick like mad, and I expect it's the same thing."

"Quite right. It is true the balance strap doesn't always go so very far back, and some horses do not mind it being tight as much as others. But I have seen the quietest horse in the world kick the stars out of the sky, and another try and lie down because the balance strap was rather far back and rather tight. The first one did not play up until after the saddle had been on a little while, but another might have done so at once.

"Now look, we'll lead Alexander about for a few minutes and let him get the feel of the different saddle, then we'll pop Merrie up and you shall see how she ought to sit—I wouldn't take a chance with a nervy pony, but Alexander won't make a fuss, particularly as she has no skirt to frighten him."

69

Philip walked and trotted Alexander for a few minutes and then Uncle Joe made him stand facing the pony with his hand on the noseband. Merrie placed her *left* foot in the palm of Uncle Joe's hand but did not press on it, reached up towards the pommel, and at the word "go" let herself be lightly swung into the saddle, giving her body a slight twist which brought her round with her right leg ready to be placed over the pommel.

"Marvellous!" cried Uncle Joe. "Never thrown up a springier lady in my life! Now gather up your reins and let's see you sitting straight. How does it feel?"

Merrie gathered the reins into her two hands, which she dropped in her lap and sat up very straight, looking ahead between Alexander's interested ears. Her left leg lay against the saddle, with the heel down, very much as it had when she was astride, and the right one hung straight down on the other side of the pommel, *not* crooked round it.

"It's just luck that the stirrup happened to be the right length," continued Uncle Joe. "It usually wants to be about the same length as it would if you were astride. You look as if you were master of all you survey!"

"Let's go on," said Merrie.

"All right. Feel your pony's mouth and touch him with your heel, and *keep your shoulders straight*, don't let one be turned farther forward than the other. Good!"

Off they went, Uncle Joe leading Alexander, and finally running along with Merrie bumping the saddle and wondering if she would eventually be swung off.

"In time you'll learn to sit beautifully still at the trot, or else to rise to it, and you'll enjoy the easiness of the canter," said Uncle Joe. "But you must keep your left leg in the same position as you would if you were astride, your heel down and your shoulders straight. Come on, Philip, you and Davy shall each have a go, but first of all tell me why Alexander seems a better side-saddle pony than Mayflower—some points to look for."

"Well," said Philip, trying to think what struck him most. "Merrie looked right in the *middle* of Alexander."

"That's one way of putting it!" Uncle Joe laughed. "You've

hit the nail on the head, however. A good side-saddle horse or pony ought really to have sufficient length of back and depth of shoulder to achieve two things: one, that the rider is not right over the 'wheels', that is to say, too near the front or hind legs, and won't be jarred by them; two, that when she is sitting up there with both legs on one side and all this contraption of pommels, she should have something in front of her—a good shoulder, not too short a neck and sufficient length of rein.

"That's the ideal, but there's many a horse, cob or pony who's got such nice paces, or carriage or temperament that he makes up in this way for other faults. He should, however, have a good strong back, well ribbed up, not a narrow sort of watershed of a back, or a hole near his loins where he looks as if he were short of a rib. That's good sense, isn't it? Here—what's this?"

As he finished speaking, Davy was seen moving off into a canter on the obliging Alexander, having climbed on to the saddle as if he were mounting astride. It must be admitted that he cantered remarkably well, keeping his hands low.

"Serve you right if he'd put you down!" declared Uncle Joe on his return. "Neither of you know a thing about cantering in a side-saddle yet. Now come and look at the rest of the saddlery and we'll get to work on *cleaning*. I'm tired of talking—here, Davy, tell us something about these girths."

"The string girth's nice and cool on a hot day, and looks marvellous when it's been washed and whitened and dried. I always like to use two of the canvas or web girths since the day I put one old one on and it broke. You clean them by letting them dry and brushing them hard. I don't know much about the other two."

"The leather girths are the strongest and they are very easy to clean," said Uncle Joe. "This folded leather one is grand if you flatten it and clean it inside and out with a damp sponge, then rub it hard with a leather, making sure it's soft and that there's not a scrap of dried sweat or grit on it. You put it on folded, with the open edges facing towards the pony's tail.

"This twisted leather girth is the kind of thing which used to be used with polo ponies a lot because it was so strong, but so narrow it did not interfere with their action and caused the minimum of

71

girth galls. You see there are two buckles at the top attaching it to the saddle, which is doubly safe, and the kind of spliced or plaited appearance makes it narrow but flat, comfortable and very strong—and very easily cleaned."

Philip picked up the rugs. "This is for the night, I suppose," he said, pointing to a very strongly made one of jute, lined with a thicker material and bound at the ends.

"Yes," said Uncle Joe. "It doesn't show the dirt too much if you shake it out well in the morning, and give it a good brushing. It must be soaked for two or three days in a tub of water, scrubbed and hung up to drain before you put it away in the summer."

Philip then picked up a lovely thick stable blanket.

"That's for wear in the day. If it is very cold and your pony is clipped out you can put the night rug on underneath it in the day, and put it underneath the night rug in the night, if you are short of covering. Otherwise, put an extra blanket underneath each.

"Now here are the surcingles. Look, one is something like a narrow light girth and that is called the jumping surcingle and is sometimes put on over a saddle to steady it in case a girth broke. Or it can be used for all sorts of things.

"The other is the surcingle proper with pads on it which your pony wears over his rug. Come on, Davy, tell us what the pads are for and how to put on the surcingle and rugs."

"You've got to put the rugs on very well forward and then pull them back a bit, but not too much," said Davy. "You don't want to rub the pony's hair up the wrong way. And you must never, never, NEVER let the edge of the rug work back during the night and rub his withers sore. Dad says he once had a horse whose bone got injured because his withers had been rubbed so often."

"Yes," said Uncle Joe. "And when you put on the surcingle which is to hold the rugs in place, put it sufficiently far forward, just about where the girths of the saddle would go, and girth it moderately tight, but make very sure the rugs are not wrinkled or folded under it. It is usually a good thing to put a folded bit of blanket, or a substantial roll of hay or straw under the pads on the surcingle to raise them up a bit, and to make sure that the surcingle itself does not, and cannot, touch the spine at all."

72

To finish off a day's real hard study of everything to do with ponies the three children settled down to tack-cleaning and this is what they did.

They hung up the bridles on a big hook hanging from the roof and washed the bits—they had wiped the bits over directly they removed them or it would have taken twice as long to clean them —then dried and rubbed them well.

The entire head-piece of the bridle, especially the underneath side, was rubbed and re-rubbed with a sponge tightly squeezed out of clean water to remove sweat and dust, and so were the reins, with long, sweeping movements. Then a different and dry sponge was rubbed on the slightly damped saddle soap and literally massaged into the leather, followed by a rare polish with the stable chamois leather.

The noseband was then placed *outside* around the head-piece, the reins passed through the throat lash and the whole hung in the saddle room.

One of the children's saddles was leather-lined, and the part which came against the horse was carefully wiped to remove all dried sweat, then thoroughly polished with the leather, but not soaped. The panels were cleaned inside and out and the entire outside of the saddle wiped, soaped and polished.

Stirrup irons were taken off, wiped and rubbed bright. Here a little Bluebell polish was permitted. The short metal bar from which they hung on the saddle sometimes got a wipe with an oily rag, and Uncle Joe had given them a tiny sewing-machine oil can filled with castor oil, from which they squeezed a drop on to the tongues of the buckles occasionally.

Leathers were hung up and very heartily wiped, soaped and rubbed. Then replaced on the saddle, with the irons run up.

Leather girths were hung from a hook, wiped absolutely clean and thoroughly rubbed and polished with a tiny bit of soap on the outside but not the inside. Mayflower's two web girths were carefully brushed—they would get an occasional thorough wash, but not every day.

As Davy's saddle had a linen, not a leather lining, that had been well brushed and just the sweat marks wiped off with a sponge thoroughly wrung out of clean water. It was then stood on its end to dry.

The children never dropped or threw the saddles down, knowing full well that the hard floor might break the tree. When they had finished they placed the saddles on the saddle horse with the correct girth lying loose over the top of each one. They wrung the sponges out of clean water ready for next day, and had the rubber been dirty they would have done the same to that.

Later on, Uncle Joe pointed out to them that it is a good thing to change over the stirrup leathers sometimes, and leave the used pair hanging straight from a hook after they have been oiled. Also, that if at any time they were obliged to keep their saddlery in the stable, and not in the saddle-room, it is best to cover the leather with a cloth or sheet.

Saddle-rooms must be dry and airy.

CHAPTER XII

TRYING OUT A TEST

DOING things is usually more exciting than just reading about them, and I dare say that Philip, Merrie and Davy probably enjoyed the carrying out of their lessons in riding and the care of saddlery more than you have enjoyed the actual description of it all. But for all that it may help you to learn about it quickly, which is quite a help.

The summer holidays seemed to slip by terribly quickly and the three children could hardly believe they were more than half over. One lovely morning found Merrie sitting on the gate into the field, with Twinkle and Foozalum on the ground beside her, and two pieces of paper in her hand.

One of these was the card of the Pony Club tests and the other a schedule of a show and gymkhana to be held at the very end of the holidays.

She had just decided that Tests C and D were too easy—she could do D and Philip or Davy C without even trying—when, to her complete surprise, the shadow of a stranger fell across her Test card.

"Hello," said the stranger, a pleasant-looking lady. "Studying the Tests? Have you taken any of them?"

Hastily catching Foozalum, who had tied a piece of string round Twinkle's neck and was trying to pull her along, Merrie said "No," but that she thought they looked very easy.

"Good gracious," said the lady, rather surprised. "Candidates are often rather nervous of them. How old are you? Eight? And you want to take D? Let's read about it.

"*Mount, dismount and ride off a leading rein on a quiet pony. Lead a pony in hand* is what is written here and sounds simple enough. The thing is, can you do it all properly and do you understand the whys and wherefores?"

Merrie tried her very hardest not to look even the tiniest bit contemptuous, and said: "If you'll watch Foozalum, I'll show you."

"Is Foozalum this adorable little heather-coloured foal?"

"No, that's Twinkle. Foozie is my brother."

"I expect you've been riding a long time, so test D will be easy for you," suggested the strange lady.

In view of the short time she had been riding this remark touched on rather a delicate point. However, nothing daunted, Merrie explained the situation.

"I *have* been on and off other people's ponies several times this year, but I have only been riding *seriously* for the last few weeks."

The lady raised her eyebrows, evidently thinking that Merrie was rather too cocksure of her ability to pass even the simple Test D. Very much on her mettle but with a tiny twinge of doubt creeping into her mind, Merrie ran off to get Sambo and his saddle and bridle, earning the lady's approval by the way she put them on.

Giving Sambo a loving pat, she faced the lady with her arm through his rein and proceeded to give her a lecture at great speed.

"When I am standing, or altering a stirrup or girthing up I always keep my arm through my pony's rein in case he should move off. When I want to get mounted, I gather the reins in my left hand, taking care not to pull on his mouth, or to have one side frightfully loose and the other frightfully tight. Then I put that hand on his withers and face his tail, stick my left foot in his stirrup, put my right hand over the flat part of the saddle and hop round and up."

She suited the action to the words very neatly, quickly taking the reins in both hands, and sitting very straight, with hands and heels down. Then she returned the reins to one hand, took both feet out of the stirrups and vaulted lightly off.

"Excellent," said the lady. "Why did you hold the middle of the saddle, not the back?"

"Uncle Joe says that on a rather high pony, or one difficult to mount, I might have to, but I mustn't if I can help it because it pulls the saddle out of place."

While she was standing, Merrie ran her stirrups up, so firmly had Uncle Joe impressed on her the necessity of making a habit

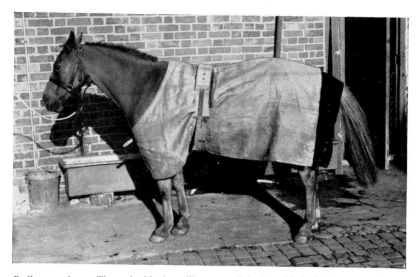

Badly rugged up. The under blanket will soon work back and fall off, the top rug has not been put on far enough forward and will quickly cause a bad sore by cutting into the pony's withers. The sercingle pad is on one side and will not prevent the surcingle from pressing on the spine. The rug is wrinkled where the two ends of the surcingle meet. These two ends should *overlap* and both must be flat.

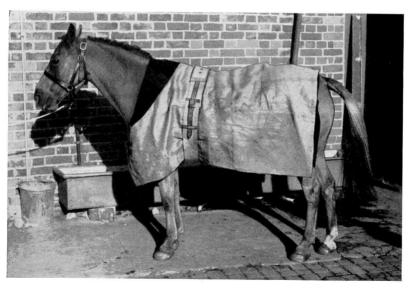

Correctly rugged. Under blanket is put on right forward and turned back. The front of the top rug reaches several inches up the neck in front of the withers so that even if it slips back a little is unlikely to cause sores. The surcingle is in the correct position with ends overlapping smoothly.

Practising reining back, using hand and leg. The toe is turned out a little too much and the pony's head is not straight, but she is obedient to the bit and does not open her mouth.

Aiming straight at the jump but rider has her stirrups a shade short and is sitting a little too much on the back of the saddle, otherwise good.

of this action at all times. Then she exclaimed: "Oh, and I forgot to say I must be careful not to touch the pony with my foot when it passes over his quarters, either mounting or dismounting, or it may upset him. And I may not dismount by swinging my leg over his neck."

"Let's see you ride," suggested the lady, and Merrie did not take long to get back in the saddle. She spoke to Sambo, shortened her reins a shade and sent him along with her legs, all in what seemed like one movement.

He walked very nicely on a comparatively loose but not flapping rein. A further slight shortening of the rein and another touch with the legs sent him into a trot. Merrie trotted across the field in as straight a line as she could, then gently—no jerking—carried out two surprisingly neat little circles at the trot, returned to her straight line and cantered back light-heartedly to her starting-point.

Very proud of Sambo's good behaviour, Merrie spoke to him, closed her legs gently—not, of course, with any suspicion of a kick, but just to bring his hocks under him—and felt his mouth with a definite give and take, to slow down his forehand or front half. He stopped really well, not too abruptly and with no jerkiness or head throwing, and he was standing nice and straight on all four legs, not sprawling about.

"Isn't he a good boy?" said Merrie, with pride. "And now look what he'll do."

She straightened herself, shortened the reins, and at the same time gave him gentle pressure with her legs. Somewhat surprised, he did not instantly respond, but more give and take with the reins and an increased leg pressure ending in very gentle prods or kicks soon made him realize, and he backed two or three paces very nicely.

He got another pat for his pains and Merrie did not trouble him any further. She had caused him to stand straight, with all his strength and muscle collected and poised like an athlete, then her leg pressure had told him to move into action and her hands had prevented him from going forward by means of gentle give-and-take, so he had gone back. There had never been the remotest question of her *pulling* him back.

"Well!" said the strange lady. "You certainly managed your

77

pony very well indeed, which is quite the most important of all. Just a *little* more practice in sitting down at the canter would be a good thing, wouldn't it?"

"Oh, it would—I know it would," said Merrie. "I will work very hard at that. Uncle Joe gives us an old glove to sit on sometimes and Philip keeps it beautifully in place. We may not put it right at the back because Uncle Joe says that would make us lean back on our behinds instead of getting down into the saddle."

"I used to have to hold a glove between my thigh and the saddle sometimes," said the lady. "Are you going to lead your pony in hand, just to complete Test D?"

"Oh yes." Merrie jumped off, and keeping her arm through the reins, ran up both stirrups. Then she drew the reins over Sambo's head, spoke to him and moved off, looking ahead of her, not looking at him, holding both reins with her right hand about a foot from his mouth, with the end in the other hand. In this way, there was no sagging loop in which either Merrie or Sambo could have caught their foot.

After they had gone a few yards, the strange lady called: "Turn now," which Merrie did instantly, but instead of turning left, which would mean that Sambo's quarters would have swung out and he would have circled more or less on top of her, she turned right, which meant that she was on the outside and Sambo on the inside of the turn.

"Grand!" said the lady. "When I was a little girl my father was for ever reminding me that I must always turn with my pony inside, but it wasn't until one trod on me and another broke away that I remembered."

At that moment Uncle Joe and the two boys made an appearance and the lady turned to him with a smile, as Merrie exclaimed: "Here's Uncle Joe."

"I must congratulate you on your remarkably thorough grounding of this young lady," said the stranger. "And may I introduce myself as Moyra Meyrick. I am staying down here for a while and Mrs. Brown, the commissioner of your branch of the Pony Club, suggested that perhaps you would be willing to accept a pony of mine as a paying guest."

Thoroughly interested, the children gathered round. "I am sure we will if we possibly can," promised Uncle Joe. "Let's hear more about it."

"Well, I'm a Pony Club instructor and I sometimes take some of the tests. As I am having a few weeks' holiday in your lovely county I promised to give some small displays with my Anglo-Arab, Hyacinthe, but I don't know where to keep her, as there is no livery stable near by."

"This couldn't be bettered," declared Uncle Joe. "You will perhaps give us some good advice about the Tests—I have never watched any, yet—and we will carefully look after your Hyacinthe. Splendid for the children, who have had little to do with feeding stabled horses as yet."

Miss Meyrick looked rather dubious.

"The only thing is that Hyacinthe is quite good-tempered, but she is a bit ticklish, doesn't like flies, and isn't really used to—to having many children about at a time."

"Better and better," said Uncle Joe. "It's all been too easy for them. I wanted them to learn something about a more complicated type of animal than their own friendly ponies. But I'll see your Hyacinthe isn't worried by them, I promise. When can you bring her?"

"Would to-morrow do?"

"Splendid. We'll roll out the red carpet, and have a chin-wag about the lady's diet."

"Have the boys taken any Tests yet?"

"No, what do you think about C for both of them?"

"Well," said Miss Meyrick, "I haven't seen them ride, or even handle their ponies, and I do not know if they understand how to look after them, though I expect they do."

"I see you've got the book of words. Read the description of Test C, Merrie," ordered Uncle Joe.

"*Riding.—Should have a seat independent of the reins and be able to maintain the correct seat and position of the hands. Have control of the pony with a knowledge of the correct aids in elementary movements, i.e., turns on the move, circles, increase and decrease of pace.*

"Stable Management.—(1) *Know the essential grooming kit and*

79

its uses. (2) *Be capable of saddling, bridling and rugging up.* (3) *Have an elementary understanding of the care and cleaning of saddlery.* (4) *Have an elementary understanding of feeding, watering and cleaning the horse."*

"Very sensible sort of Test," declared Uncle Joe. "If all those things can be done really properly, the kids have a grounding which will make it easy for them to go right ahead. What do you think about it, you two boys?"

"I guess I can do most of the things, but I don't know if I can do them well enough," said Philip.

"Mayflower's very quick about going faster and slower," said Davy, thinking of the increase and decrease of pace.

"More to it than that, old chap," said Uncle Joe with a wry smile. "Actually you should both make a fair job of that Test, except that Philip's knowledge of feeding and watering a stabled horse is mostly theory, though I suppose Davy's had some practical experience."

"Well, Philip will be able to tell us something about keeping ponies at grass. Shall we have a try-out Test to-morrow when I bring Hyacinthe, or is that not convenient?"

"Oh yes, do let's." All were delighted with the idea and, shortly after, Miss Meyrick took her leave.

CHAPTER XIII

ABOUT TWINKLE AND FEEDING

IT seems rather a shame that up to now so little has been said about Twinkle, the four-months-old Dartmoor foal who came back with the children from the sale. Miss Meyrick's speaking of her as "heather-coloured" reminded me that you might like some details.

If Twinkle had been turned out in a big park with a lot of other young stock there is no doubt that she would have remained wild quite a long time. But Sambo's paddock was not as big as all that, and Sambo was quite a middle-aged pony, well used to human beings.

When Twinkle who, after all, had only had four months of being wild, and who had a very inquisitive nature, saw Sambo go up and talk to Merrie and receive tit-bits whenever she came into the field, she did not take long to come sniffing round, too, particularly as Merrie never tried to catch her or even pat her until she was so used to her that Twinkle thought nothing of it.

In a few weeks after her arrival Twinkle was quite happy to play with Foozalum and they would even lie in the grass together, although if Foozie got too rough or over-friendly, Twinkle would dart quickly away, sometimes rolling Foozie over in the process.

Twinkle was very happy now. She was leading a natural sort of free life, otherwise she would never have been a safe companion for as young a child as Foozie, and she was only a small pony-foal, not the foal of a big horse, who might have been rather large and clumsy and perhaps might have hurt him.

As Miss Meyrick had said, Twinkle *was* heather-coloured, a curious and charming shade which would probably turn black as she grew older. Foozle was never left alone with her, although they played together quite a lot with someone to keep an eye on them and to see that Foozie did not tease and get himself kicked or bitten for his pains.

On the day after Merrie's experiment with D Test Miss Meyrick arrived at the field with a small terrier and a very beautiful Anglo-Arab. The small terrier ran up to Twinkle, who was not well used to dogs and was rather taken by surprise.

However, firmly spoken to by Miss Meyrick, it did not bark at her, and before long they were at play, Twinkle chasing the little dog until Miss Meyrick called him in. She was afraid that both might get over-excited and that there would be too much "horse play", which might lead to Twinkle becoming unreliable with dogs, and the little terrier inclined to rush or snap at ponies.

"Oh, isn't she marvellous?" This was Merrie, enraptured by the Anglo-Arab, who was a lovely rich chestnut in colour, with the thrilling lines of a thorough-bred in her body and limbs, and a head with the wide brow, generous eye and alert ears of an Arab.

Davy appeared from the stable with a pitchfork in his hand. "We've got your box ready—look."

He and Philip might well feel proud of themselves. The box had been thoroughly washed before breakfast and left open to the winds of heaven to dry out for several hours; then deeply bedded down with fresh straw, well tossed and pressed into place with a fork, so that the ends were not all lying the one way and would not wreathe themselves too much round the new inhabitant's legs.

A clean bucket of fresh water stood in a corner and a hay-net filled with rich, fresh-smelling hay hung beside the manger, well out of the way and just high enough to make it unlikely that a horse would catch his foot in it even if he stamped or rolled.

"Uncle Joe said you might not arrive at a feed time, but to put a bit of hay in the box to make your pony settle," announced Philip.

At this moment Uncle Joe himself arrived, full of praises of the newcomer. "Never seen a real Anglo-Arab before," he announced. "We don't see enough of them over here."

"No," agreed Miss Meyrick. "Lots of part-bred Arabs, but few Anglo-Arabs, which are the offspring of a thoroughbred and a pure

Arab. They are most carefully bred in France and that's where I got Hyacinthe."

"You must tell us all about her sometime. She only stands about three or four inches higher than Alex, I see. Well, it's twelve-thirty, and the lady's lunch-time, I expect. We've got most things here, so say what's to be got ready."

"A couple of double handfuls of chaff, two or three pounds of oats and about a pound of raw carrots chopped small, all mixed well together, will do her beautifully after she has had a nice drink of water, and with all that hay to follow," declared Miss Meyrick.

They took Hyacinthe inside, removed her saddle and bridle, and put on her summer-sheet, or dust-sheet. This cotton-mixture sheet not only keeps away the dust, helps the fine summer coat of a horse to lie flat and smooth, but is a protection from flies into the bargain.

The children were not allowed to go into the box and worry Hyacinthe, except for Philip, who spoke to her to warn her of his coming and took in her feed. She was to be left alone for a couple of hours to eat and digest it.

Outside, Miss Meyrick, who had been introduced to Alex and Mayflower, questioned them on the feeding of ponies generally. "Now, let's take Alex," she said. "Supposing he was living in a stable and doing an average day's work, how would you feed him?"

"Well," said Philip, "I suppose I'd probably give him an armful of hay—a couple of pounds—and about half a bucket of water if I was going to ride him first thing in the morning. He could eat it while I was 'quartering him over', as Uncle Joe calls it—knocking the worst dirt off him—and perhaps starting to muck out.

"Then when we came in from our ride I'd give him his proper breakfast while I had mine, at about half-past eight. I'd give him a double handful of chaff, a couple of pounds of oats, and the same amount of hay, which would have to last him till midday when he'd get the same amount of chaff, two pounds of oats, one pound of carrots or chopped mangel-wurzels or swedes, but no hay.

"He'd get another feed about four p.m. and one about seven or eight p.m. if I could manage it, with about eight pounds of hay to

83

play with during the night, and a nice full bucket of water handy."

"Yes," said Miss Meyrick. "But supposing he could never be fed more than three times a day? I know four or even five times is very much better for their stomachs and more natural."

"Oh, if I *wasn't* going to ride him early, but at about ten o'clock, I'd give him his first feed of three pounds of oats, two double handfuls of chaff and a pound or so of bran about seven a.m. with about a couple of pounds of hay to follow.

"Then another at about twelve-thirty, with two pounds of oats, and chaff plus the chopped carrots. Perhaps a bite of hay if he wanted it. And a final go about six p.m.: three pounds of oats this time with perhaps nine pounds of hay. Of course he'd have to have more of something else and less oats if eight pounds of oats a day made him too saucy."

"You've got it all very well taped," said Miss Meyrick. "If your pony only gets three feeds a day much the best thing to do, if possible, is to give him only a little hay after his five-thirty or six p.m. feed, and then a good watering and all the bulk of his hay about nine or ten p.m.

"Horses or ponies have small stomachs and large intestines and their natural way of feeding is little and often. They need—they must have—a lot of water to drink—five to fifteen gallons is what the Army manual says—and they should never be hurried over their drinking. If fed only three times a day and given a large meal at midday, they *must* have plenty of time, alone and quiet, to digest it."

They went on talking for some time about feeding, but most of what they said can be found in the Appendix. After lunch the two boys were to practise Test C riding with Miss Meyrick to see if they were going on the right lines. She would not be taking either the C or D Tests on the Test Day, only the A and B, so no one could think it unfair of her to give them instruction.

Reining back. Rider in good position, pony straight.

Here is Jennie Bullen riding side-saddle in a pair class at a show, with her brother. She is sitting with her shoulders straight, not slightly twisted to one side, and her stirrup leather is about the same length as it would be if she was riding astride.

Pony is being asked to change from leading off (right) fore and near (left) hind to near fore and off hind, and is just doing so.

Turning slightly to the right at the canter. Rider is driving his pony on with leg and heel pressure, but is sitting too much on the back of the saddle and is not sufficiently upright.

Practising for the Test under the eye of Uncle Joe

CHAPTER XIV

MORE TEST PRACTICE

" As I've never had anything to do with the Pony Club Tests before, I think I'll tell the boys what I'd like to see them do, and you shall tell me if I'm wrong," said Uncle Joe after lunch.

In no time at all Philip and Davy arrived with Alex and Mayflower and gave a very good display of mounting and dismounting. Then, standing in the middle of the little practice ground or manège in the paddock, he rode Alex round at a trot and canter both with and without his stirrups and his reins, in order to prove that his "seat was independent of the reins".

Philip used his legs and his voice very well to get Alex going round the manège, as once he had started down the side he had no reins to collect or guide him. Just for the fun of it, Alex put in a playful and comparatively harmless plunge or buck quite unexpectedly, and he had to gather up the reins quickly to steady and straighten him, which he did very smoothly and well—no jerks of body or hands.

"I don't think we can send the saucy little Mayflower round

85

without reins," declared Uncle Joe. "So Philip shall ride Alex and lead her, while Davy rides with folded arms—it will be good practice for both Philip and Alex."

Davy did his stuff excellently, sitting up very straight, with heels down. At the end of it Miss Meyrick called both boys over.

"You led Mayflower very well," she said to Philip. "Suppose you tell me some of the secrets of leading a pony safely and successfully?"

"Well, I should think one of them is to be sure and keep them shoulder to shoulder—never let the led pony sag behind."

"How right you are," said Miss Meyrick. "Keep your ponies level and you can probably avoid kicking matches, which so often happens if one or other goes ahead. And watch the head of both your own horse and the one you lead, so that you can stop either of them from snapping at the other."

As regards the correct position of the seat and hands, both boys were well down in the saddle, after having been worked on tirelessly by Uncle Joe, who had made them do plenty of exercises and riding without stirrups. One of his favourite tests had been to get them to let their legs hang absolutely straight down from the hip when they were in the saddle, and then very gradually raise them, keeping them flat against the saddle, until they automatically reached the correct knee position.

Philip carried his hands very well—low, with slightly rounded, flexible wrists and the knuckles and nails nearly facing one another, but just a little inclined to slant downwards. Davy was apt to be a bit careless with his hands, which seemed to find their way into several unusual positions, but at least he was never heavy-handed.

"Now let Miss Meyrick see your increase and decrease of pace," said Uncle Joe. "First of all, move off at a walk, and start to trot when I shout."

Here again Philip was at an advantage, although Alex was young and not yet well trained. But he worked steadily and smoothly upon him, no jerky, hurried movements, and consequently Alex was never unbalanced and moved off into his different paces or change of gait very pleasantly—positively flowed into them. In dressage terms he would have been said to have been "smooth in his transitions".

Not so with poor Davy. He was always inclined to be a little slap-dash and Mayflower equally ready to get excited. To cap it all, on this occasion Davy felt a shade nervy.

Consequently when Uncle Joe shouted to him to trot, he fairly flapped the reins and gave Mayflower a hearty kick. Mayflower went off as if she were in for a trotting race, and would probably have got quite out of hand but that everyone yelled to Davy to stop immediately and start again.

Here, alas, there was another failure, as this time Davy closed his legs so feebly Mayflower did not even know he meant to do it, and he kept such a firm hold on her mouth she could not get started.

However, everyone laughed so heartily, but in such a friendly way, that he found himself doing the same, forgot his nerves and moved off quite passably well, without thinking too much about it. I am afraid he had some difficulty in keeping Mayflower at a slow canter because of his almost incurable habit of letting her get out of hand to start with.

Miss Meyrick called him in to talk it over. "I should think your keen pony has quite a nice mouth, hasn't she?"

"Oh yes, she answers at once," said Davy proudly.

"Think a moment then," said Miss Meyrick. "If you let her believe you are willing for her to go fast, and then hang on for dear life, or else take a lot of hard pulls to stop her, aren't you going just the right way to ruin her mouth?"

This idea had never struck Davy, who had been inclined to consider the necessity for steadying a pony in good time rather a pansy way of riding.

"See what you can do about it," suggested Miss Meyrick. "You'll probably be able to ride Mayflower with a looser rein and more freedom if you try and do without all sharp acceleration and sudden braking!"

"You can ride your pony very well when you like, old boy," said Uncle Joe. "You must just make a habit of it and then you'll find you always do it without having to think. We must practise the increase and decrease of speed and carefully avoid all jerkiness."

The two boys then set about the elementary movements, for which they were expected to know the correct aids. First of all, they circled the manège, changing rein quarter-way round. This meant that when they were quarter-way down one side they changed direction, going diagonally across the centre of the school to the opposite corner, then swinging round not too abruptly and continuing the circle in the opposite direction to the one in which they started, like this:

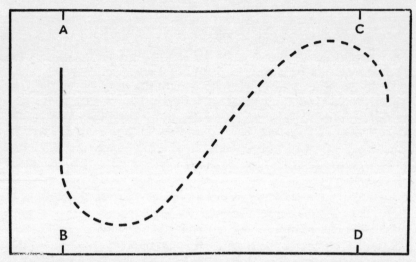

Changing rein. Pony crosses the school or manège instead of going on round it

Now if they were cantering round to the right with the right or off fore leg leading and were keeping a nice contact with their pony, all they had to do was to feel the right rein, let the left or indirect rein act as a slight support against the neck, to help keep the pony straight, and give a strong feel with the left leg.

Then as they approached the opposite corner they would use exactly the opposite aids or indications. In some cases it might be necessary to collect the pony before telling him to change leg, but it was not necessary in this case, as the pony was already sufficiently collected. That is to say, he was "on the bit" and his hocks were under him, all set for the rider's command. The rider kept just a light, a really light contact, and the pony went up to the bit, felt it, accepted it, knew it would tell him what was wanted.

Therefore to change on to the left leg, the children increased their feel of their ponies' mouths with both reins the tiniest bit, to steady them and tell them what was coming; then felt the left rein definitely, using the right rein as a support, and giving extra pressure (or even a slight kick, if absolutely necessary) with the right leg, just behind the girth. The other leg can give a tiny pressure to keep the pony going on and going straight, if this is required, but must never, never move out of position or be used as strongly as the one which is giving the orders.

These indications should drive the pony into leading with his left or near hind and fore legs just in time to turn the corner left round the manège. You see, he would thus be leading on the inside legs, the reason for this being that this side will have to support the sharpest part of the turn. It is most important that he should change with his hind as well as his fore leg.

This is quite a stiff practice, as a number of things have to be done quickly—the pony turned across the school, kept straight in the right direction, and asked to change leg just as he *starts* to make a graceful, sweeping circle round the corner. It must never be a sharp, jerky turn and he must never be asked to change leg too late, i.e. when he is half-way round it.

All three ponies had a go, and very well they did it, because their riders were quite sure what they wanted them to do and did not fuss or confuse them. It is very difficult for a pony if his rider is a bit uncertain. In a way, riding is like dancing, rider and pony must keep in time together smoothly, and it is useless to try difficult steps until one can do easy ones correctly. And just as in dancing you don't look down at your feet, you must not look down at your pony's leading leg; you must learn to know by the feel which leg he is on and what changes he is going to make.

Philip rode Alex, keeping contact, but not attempting to collect him too much as he was still too young and green. He told him definitely what he wanted at the right moment and the pony did it. That is half the secret of good riding, to know and feel by the movement of the pony the right moment to tell him to change leg for the turn you see ahead of you, or whatever else you are going to ask him to do.

Davy was on his mettle and, despite his earlier mistakes over the

89

much simpler test, really rode Mayflower beautifully. He kept a nice contact and Mayflower, who had certainly been well schooled at some time, was nicely collected, not sprawling about, and did everything so smoothly and easily that it was a pleasure to see.

Merrie and Sambo were also very good. She made no attempt to interfere with the way he carried his head, and once or twice she had to give small kicks rather than leg pressure only, but all the same she got the results without any unnecessary use of leg or hand, and this is all that is expected.

After this practice in the manège they all went out into the field, to practise riding about in a more open space and to carry out turns and circles, all of which they were made to do slowly.

"I don't know whether you agree with me that if a child can ride a straight line he will probably have little difficulty with a circle?" Uncle Joe asked of Miss Meyrick.

"Well, I suppose it depends on his or her sense of direction a bit. Some children, and grown-ups, too, have no sense of direction. But I believe you are right, because if they can ride a straight line it means that they know how to direct their pony the way they want to go."

"I think it is one of the most important practices any child can carry out," said Uncle Joe. He placed three stones about twenty-five yards apart and made the children first walk, then trot and then canter past them, afterwards riding what they imagined to be a straight line with only a distant tree as a guide.

"We'll just have one practice of stopping, and then that will do for to-day," said Miss Meyrick. She stood in the middle of the field and each child in turn walked, trotted and cantered up to her, with the idea of stopping exactly beside her.

Actually, what happened at the first attempt was that Sambo, who had a very good idea of what was afoot, stopped beside Miss Meyrick with very little effort on Merrie's part. He received a laugh and a pat and looked very pleased with himself. Alex went past her, because Philip did not want to stop him too suddenly and rather miscalculated the distance. Mayflower did stop exactly in the right place but perhaps with rather a jerk and more by good luck than good judgment.

"I think you've probably got the idea now," said Miss Meyrick.

"But just remember that to stop (not to start) you must close your legs and bring your pony's hocks under him to act as a brake one split second before you use your hands—only one second, though. Then he will stop *so* much more easily and neatly, and he will be up to his bridle or on the bit, all ready to start off again."

Davy looked most interested and evidently figured that this method should make it easier to stop dead on line. He put it into practice by closing his legs so sharply that he startled Mayflower and consequently jerked her mouth trying to stop her, which brought a severe reprimand.

Philip, although the green and as yet inexperienced Alex was never as collected and on the spot as Mayflower, managed to stop him surprisingly accurately and with remarkably little trouble.

Miss Meyrick called them over for a final chat before they turned the ponies loose.

"I think you've all done very well," she said. "Yesterday Merrie gave me a really fine display of reining back, but I want you to realize that this is not expected in Test D. In C there will be no complicated figures-of-eight, just simple turns and circles, and all you have to think of is carrying them out smoothly and sensibly, just exactly as you would do if you were out on an ordinary ride.

"If you think what you are doing, find out the reason for it and always think of your pony first in your every-day riding, you will have nothing to worry about in the Tests. I'd like you to remember one thing. It is true that your three ponies are completely different, which will help you to realize all the different things which need to be noticed and thought about. But they are fairly straightforward ponies that don't give you any bad difficulties; whereas some children have ponies of an impossible shape, or hard mouths, or funny temperaments. Very often they have to do things rather differently from the way you are taught to do them. Kick, instead of close their legs, for example. Ride with a much looser rein, perhaps. Because of this, don't you do either of two things, criticize them, or become careless in your own way of riding! And do remember that the main principles of good riding are never wrong. They may have to be modified or altered just a little to suit individual cases, but the less you do it the better. People who do it too much are definitely wrong."

91

CHAPTER XV

HOW THEY DID AT THE SHOW

IT was quite unbearably exciting! The Three Great Days of the summer holidays would all take place in the last week or so before school started again—the local show, the Tests and a day's cub-hunting!

To make everything even more breath-taking, Uncle Joe seemed quite uncertain whether he would let Philip and Merrie enter for any of the gymkhana events at the show in case these games on horseback made them rough or careless in their riding.

"If you had been at it a bit longer and got all your good habits nicely settled, I should think nothing of it," he declared. "But after all, you've only been riding a short time, though I grant you that you've worked very hard. I would rather have waited till after the Tests."

Eventually he gave way and allowed both of them to enter their ponies in the right height classes—12 hands 2 inches and 13 hands 2 inches—in an egg and spoon race and the musical chairs, declaring quite firmly that neither they nor their ponies were ready for the bending race or the jumping.

The children were up very early on the day of the show, and a lovely day it was, not too hot but filled with the golden glow of September.

Merrie knew quite well that Sambo's big joint would make it very unlikely that he would get a prize even if she rode him well enough, and Philip knew that Alexander could hardly beat ponies like Rowan, but they took a great pride in making them both look as nice as possible. All the saddlery had been carefully cleaned the night before and was then covered up. The ponies were groomed and polished very thoroughly, their tails brushed and brushed, and their manes plaited—not too tightly—with the ends turned under-neath and secured with a needle and thread. The fact that they were at grass most of the time and were already changing from their summer to their winter coat made them look a little less polished than the stabled show ponies, but none the less they were a great credit to the children.

Uncle Joe said he would bring the ponies' feeds and a bucket for water in the car, otherwise they would have had to carry them in bags attached to the front of the saddle. He also brought head-collars and ropes, their summer sheets to keep them clean and protect them from flies, a sponge, brush, a clean stable rubber and a hoof-pick in case they should pick up a stone or anything else on the way. He looked both children over carefully—clean boots, well-brushed jodhpurs, neat shirt, tie, coat, hat, string gloves (mended!) and stick.

They started in good time to ride the three miles to the show, allowing an hour and a half in case of any delays and so that their ponies should get accustomed to the ground and crowd before they went into the ring.

Merrie's class was first and fifteen lovely little ponies filed into the ring. The one just in front of Merrie was a real show model, with beautiful manners, and a long smooth stride. Merrie took care to keep out of reach of its heels just in case!

She was so interested she forgot to think about herself and consequently rode freely and easily, carrying out automatically the things which Uncle Joe had made her do every day until they had become a habit.

Uncle Joe had told her to be on the alert for instructions all the time, and never to bunch but to keep clear of other ponies. Consequently when she was called she came in at once, and was delighted to find she was only about half-way down the line.

And then the most amazing thing happened! The last thing Merrie had ever expected was to be asked to go out in front of the other ponies and give a little show on her own. But after the judges had looked all the other ponies over, and after they had sent out half a dozen highly-bred and unblemished ponies, this is just what they told her to do.

In a way it was alarming, but not desperately so, as Uncle Joe had impressed on her that she must only do the simplest things and be thinking all the time of Sambo, and how to tell him what was needed, and not at all of herself or of what she looked like.

Sambo did a little walk, and a trot and a canter most beautifully. But the idea of a circle at the trot puzzled her, for the moment because the space between the ponies and the ropes round the ring was rather narrow.

However, she took him up to one end where there was a bit more room, and trotted carefully round in a smallish circle, trying to finish where she started, trotted back to the judges, pulled up, closing her legs just before she used her hands. When she came to a standstill she could feel that Sambo was standing beautifully straight and she decided to show how nicely he reined back.

The judges laughed and told her to go and stand below four of the other ponies. The rosettes were handed out and behold! Sambo had got the prize for the best local pony ridden by its owner!

It was the proudest moment of Merrie's life when she cantered round the ring, with the rosette in her mouth, and she jumped off and threw her arms round Sambo's neck as soon as she got outside. Uncle Joe arrived with a smile on his face and a carrot in his hand, but Philip and Davy could only wave to her, as they were just riding into the ring for their own class.

The Wideawakes' superb animal Rowan which the children had first seen at the Pony Club rally was competing in this event for ponies not more than 14 hands 2 inches. He stood exactly 14 hands 2 inches and every one of those inches looked perfect.

Alexander was an inch less and Mayflower seemed quite small in comparison, as she was 13 hands 2½ inches—3½ inches difference—and only just too big for the 13 hands 2 inches event.

There were lots of other good ponies in this class, but they varied rather. One looked rather like a weedy, mean-looking little thorough-bred, another was just too much of the hunter type for an ordinary show pony event, another was rather thick and stocky and another had a poor shoulder and no length of stride.

As soon as they started to canter, one pony who had been going along star-gazing, a real little Johnny-Head-in-Air, suddenly stuck in his toes and gave such a kick he sent his small rider flying. He

94

rushed by all the ponies, causing one of them to dash off, though its sensible rider quickly pulled it up.

Davy, who was on the alert, spoke gently to Mayflower, keeping contact but not making any sort of grab at the reins, and she responded beautifully. Alex and Rowan, calmed by their riders, also behaved very well. The pony was caught and the rider remounted, none the worse for the fall, but with a black mark against his mount, as good manners are expected in the ring.

When at last they were all lined up, Philip found himself next to Rowan—the great and wonderful Rowan—with Mayflower standing about three ponies lower. He could not help feeling pleased as Alex was not even fully grown-up yet, and would not be at his best for another year or two.

Rowan was the first pony called out to give a display, to show how handy and obedient and *well-educated* he was. He went very beautifully although he looked a little bored, was not quite as fresh and free in his movements as he might be.

Then it was Alex's turn. For some extraordinary reason Philip thought of him as a great General—the great General Alexander, conqueror of all opponents—and nearly burst out laughing at himself.

But the idea had a good effect as his amusement made him relax a little bit, and he went out calmly enough to give his display. Consequently he did not make his young pony nervous, nor ride it stiffly, and he had the sense not to ask it to do anything which it could not do well and easily.

Although Rowan had carried out a figure of eight, Philip contented himself very wisely with a walk, trot and canter, circle to either rein and a rein-back, walking back to his place with a loose rein, the pony carrying himself freely and well.

Of the next three ponies, all of which were very good-looking although one was rather too long in the back (which means some lack of strength), the first refused to leave the others and even reared up a little when asked to do so, the second sprawled about and gave a very untidy and "ragged" show, leading with the wrong leg at the canter (remember that if you are going to circle or even bend in one direction your pony should lead with the leg on that side), and the third gave quite a good display, but was disunited for a few paces. This means that when he changed leading legs he only changed with his front legs, not with his hind ones.

Then Mayflower came out, with Davy looking as if butter wouldn't melt in his mouth. Knowing Davy, Philip couldn't help wondering what he would do, as he could be so foolish sometimes and at others so clever. However, when he looked as smug as he did now things generally went fairly well.

This small boy and small pony seemed to be very "junior" to the rest of the class, but they were fortunately not a bit worried about it. And for once Davy had the good sense to mind his p's and q's and take no chances, without making too enormous an effort. He just behaved naturally and sensibly and gave all his attention to the pony.

Consequently an unworried and confident Mayflower, helped and guided but not forced, gave a really beautiful, simple show, just like Alex's, and returned quietly to her place.

Then came the inspection of the ponies without their saddles. When Rowan stood in front of the judges with no saddle on, even the inexperienced Philip could not help noticing that although he was beautifully made and carried himself with great pride, he was looking just the tiniest bit jaded and worn—not as smooth and sleek as he might be.

Philip ran up his stirrups, took his saddle off carefully and up-ended it on the ground; led Alex out and stood him on a nice level piece of grass between the judges and the ringside; made sure that he was standing properly on all four legs—that is to say, that he was *using* them all, that one of his hind legs wasn't sprawled too far forward—and waited with the reins held loosely but fairly high (to keep Alex's head up) for the inspection.

He was next asked to walk away from the judges and trot back past them. They wanted to see if the pony moved absolutely straight, not favouring one leg the slightest bit more than the other, and with the hind feet following exactly in the track of the fore feet. In addition to this, they had to make sure that Alex had no faulty action such as dishing, turning a toe in, etc.

Philip remembered to hold the reins in both hands and to run

He went out calmly enough

just ahead and a little to one side of the pony without looking back. He remembered, too, that when he turned round he must turn with Alex's body on the inside of the circle—not to go round with the pony outside and himself on the inner edge. It is much easier to control a pony this way, and one is far less likely to be trodden on.

When the first six ponies had been "stripped" (shown without their saddles) and run down, the judges had a consultation while they were being re-saddled. Philip longed to hear what they were saying. At last they came to a decision, and to his delight Philip saw Mayflower advancing upon him. The little mare was coming up into third place, no doubt by virtue of her free movement, balanced display, her obedience, good condition and the fact that despite one or two faults which gave her a very slightly trap-pony appearance, she was very well-made and evidently nicely bred.

97   G

Philip and Alex remained where they were. Second to the so-valuable Rowan! It seemed indeed an honour, although later in the day Uncle Joe pointed out that it was not so much the type of horse that stood above you, as the quality of the ones below—the ones you beat—which counted. Despite this, Philip was happy to be in such good company.

He and Davy felt very proud of their ponies as they rode out of the ring, particularly as the reserve, highly commended and commended animals were such good lookers.

One of them was perhaps better-made than Mayflower, but certainly did not move as well at the canter. The other was a beautiful pony although a shade "weak of its loins"—it had not a very good back. It was inclined to stick its nose out and did not bridle very well.

CHAPTER XVI

ALEXANDER OR ROWAN

WELL, the exciting happenings described in the last chapter were only what took place during the morning spent at the local show, the very first show in which either Merrie, Philip or Davy had competed, and we must try and give you a picture of the afternoon as well.

Do you suppose the children galloped around showing off their rosettes, or tied up their ponies and forgot them while they had their own lunch?

Not a bit of it. After all, Sambo, Alex and Mayflower had carried them to the show, worked quite hard in the ring, were going to compete in gymkhana events later in the day, as well as hack home in the early evening, and it would have been selfish and stupid to tire them with aimless cantering about. Besides, they were pretty hungry by now.

These three ponies had got to know each other very well and were not likely to kick unless tormented by flies, so the children took off their saddles and bridles (just as well, since Alex lay down and had a nice roll), and then tied them up by their head-collars and ropes under a shady bit of hedge a little distance away from the strange ponies.

Uncle Joe produced a bucket of water from somewhere nearby— a farm, a stream or a pond—put on the fly sheets and in a few moments they were all contentedly munching their lunch.

Egg and spoon race was not until four p.m. and the children took it in turn to keep an eye on the ponies and wander round. Somewhat to Philip's surprise, the boy, a little older than himself, who had been riding Rowan, came up to him to ask if Alex could jump.

"You bet he can," said Philip.

"Do let's see him," said the Rowan boy.

"Well, I don't know," replied Philip. There didn't seem much harm in just popping him once over a pole, but he had a feeling that perhaps Uncle Joe would find a catch in it.

However, this difficulty was solved by the appearance of Uncle Joe, who agreed to trying him over something about three feet in height. The boy, whose name turned out to be William and whose father was the Mr. Wideawake who owned Rowan, ran off to get the groom and the jump which they always brought in the horse-box in case they wanted to practise before they went into the ring.

Philip wondered just what Alex would think of this artificial-looking jump. First of all he cantered round it in a big circle once or twice to get the pony going, then swung in towards it on a nice straight line. Alex went for it as if to jump it was the one thing he wanted to do above all others, clearing it very easily. Philip let him go on for a few yards, then circled him again and drew up beside the others.

"What a jumper that pony would make if he were properly schooled," declared Mr. Wideawake. Uncle Joe smiled and said that they were quietly setting about his education and that he hoped Philip would get some good half day's hunting on him during the Christmas holidays.

"The truth of the matter is I want a useful sort of young pony, likely to win hunter trials and show-jumping, too, for my son William," said Mr. Wideawake. "Your pony caught my eye in the show pony event, and I thought I'd have a chat with you and find out what he could do. Would you consider selling him?"

For some reason this seemed to amuse Uncle Joe, who said: "For that matter, my nephew Phillip has always had his eye on your pony Rowan. Let's see what he has got to say."

When Philip arrived he was told that Mr. Wideawake would like to buy Alex, or might even consider some sort of exchange.

"What do *you* want to do, my boy?" asked Uncle Joe. "Sell or keep your pony you are training so well? Or perhaps have Rowan instead of him?"

Philip became scarlet with the effort to think it all out. "How do you feel about it, Uncle?" he said, realizing that, after all, it was Uncle Joe's money which had bought Alex.

100

"Never mind me, old boy. I'm quite happy either way."

Out of all the different things which Philip had to think of at once, just one stood out quite clearly. He felt as if there were some sort of friendship between him and the young, inexperienced pony —they had done very well together up to now. He enjoyed training him, and learnt so much from the pony in the process. He determined to go through with it and see what sort of a fist he and Alex had made of it by the time they finished—if one ever did finish.

"Rowan is a grand pony," he said. "But I'd like to keep Alex."

Uncle Joe had never looked so pleased in his life. "Good lad," he said. "Glad to see you kept your head—it must have been quite a temptation. Sorry, Mr. Wideawake, I'm sure you'll understand. The boy's training the pony. They suit each other, and he wants to go through with it. No reason why he shouldn't."

Merrie and Davy, who had been listening with ears pricked, had very strong feelings about Philip's decision. Merrie was nearly in tears with relief that Alex was not going anywhere where he would not be loved, and would perhaps be over-trained and spoilt—she sensed this probability, although she might not have been able to put it into words. Davy was merely extremely pleased to see that Mr. Wideawake could not buy every single thing he wanted in life; and that they were not going to lose Alex.

Thoroughly worked up, they trooped off to watch Miss Meyrick give a beautiful best-trained horse display with the showy Hyacinthe. They thoroughly enjoyed the smooth, swift movements and liked to think that they had seen Hyacinthe jumping and knew for themselves that, thanks to her training, she was a hundred per cent efficient at most branches of horsemanship, as well as being a heavenly ride.

"Don't suppose you'll ever reach this lady's standard," said the admiring Uncle Joe. "You won't have time while you are at school. But you are going to have a lot of fun with your pony and train him to be a useful hunter and jumper, if you go the right way about it.

"I'm very glad you are keeping Alex to train, instead of getting one that's ready made, and has been used as a machine a bit too long. Rowan is beginning to show signs of his age, too."

Merrie had a tiny twinge, wishing that Rowan could stop being "used as a machine" but was comforted when Uncle Joe happened to remark that no doubt he would soon be advertised for sale.

Egg and spoon and musical chairs caused a lot of fun, as all three children were in these events together. Alex did not know the games and did not tumble to them quite quickly enough. Davy and Mayflower forgot themselves and went off with such a burst of speed that when he dropped the egg he had little hope of picking it up again.

But Sambo surprised them all. He had evidently played egg and spoon quite often, even if Merrie had not. He broke straight away into the quietest little canter, taking no notice of the other ponies surging ahead of him, several of whose riders lost their eggs. And he won his heat! He was beaten by a little expert in the final, but got a third prize in the musical chairs—he would turn in towards a chair of his own accord as soon as the music stopped.

Uncle Joe congratulated all three children on riding quite nicely with the reins in one hand in the egg and spoon race, pointing out that it was essential that they should be equally good with one or both hands, according to what particular work they were doing.

And so ended what was indeed a red letter day.

Davy on Mayflower

CHAPTER XVII

INVITATION TO CUB-HUNTING

As if to make sure that the endurance of the children and ponies, as well as their knowledge, should receive a thorough test, it poured with rain on the Test Day, forty-eight hours later.

They arrived at the rally in mackintoshes, the rain running off their ponies' backs, and took care to keep them moving about until such time as they were called for, so that they would not get chilled. However, half-way through the morning the sun came out and they began to dry up.

Everything went off quite peacefully, the examiners were very friendly and ready to explain any particularly puzzling problems; and having their own ponies to look after and practise upon made everything much easier. Although unable to attend the Pony Club camp this year, they had not been too late to join in a couple of working rallies, so that there was no feeling of strangeness.

The Pony Club instructor, who had picked Davy up when he fell off Mayflower on the first day, thought he had improved wonderfully—there was no doubt that he had it in him to make a really clever rider. She had a chat with Philip and Merrie whom she had seen a few times but really did not know well.

In the end all three children passed their Tests—Merrie got her D Test certificate very easily—she was really quite ready for C—and Philip and Davy had nothing to worry them seriously when taking it. Both determined to work very hard for B, which is a much more searching test of riding, the care of horses, saddlery, shoeing and first aid, though not in any way complicated.

And so we come to the third and last Great Day, when all three were to go cubbing with the pack with which they hoped to hunt during the Christmas holidays. Only three more days were left before they went back to school and there was so much to do in them.

The Meet was at the Kennels at seven a.m. and the Kennels were a good half-hour's ride from the stables. The ponies were easy to catch and the field was close by the house, otherwise they would have brought them in over-night. As it was, they fetched them for a bit of a feed and brush over at about a quarter-past five, just about the time Miss Meyrick had arrived to water and feed Hyacinthe, who was coming with them. The ponies' shoes had been looked at carefully the night before to make sure all was in order, and the feeds, grooming kit and tack all put ready.

Cubbing, with its early hours—indeed it was still quite dark when the children went into the field and they were obliged to turn the light on in the stables—and the fact that it is intended to train the "young entry"—the hounds who are starting on their first season's hunting—does not need as much preparation as would a day during the real season, which usually opens on the first Monday in November.

There is a lot of hanging about, but not the long runs which can be something of an endurance test for pony and rider. And no one is expected to wear any but the simplest clothes—jodhpurs, polo-sweaters—"rat-catcher" check coats—unless they prefer breeches and boots.

Consequently neither pony nor rider need so much preparation, and they know they will probably not go nearly as far from home as they would in an ordinary day's hunting.

Not only does cubbing help to teach the hounds their job but it helps gradually to get fit the horses or ponies who have been turned out during the summer and will be hunting continuously throughout the season.

On this occasion the children ate a quick breakfast while the ponies were finishing theirs, had a wash and started off eagerly. Uncle Joe went with them on a nice grey cob and Miss Meyrick and Hyacinthe made up the party.

Uncle Joe allowed them an occasional short trot, but pointed out that if they had really been going hunting they would have had to walk their ponies most of the way, in order to save their strength for the business ahead. He also explained that the trot carried out by the horses of the Hunt servants when exercising hounds, or taking them to and from Kennels, was usually known as a "hound trot" and was at the rate of about six miles an hour.

A few people had been invited to the Meet but not a great number —too big a field is a nuisance at a cubbing Meet—and they quickly moved off to the first covert, the hounds in good order. The children said "good morning" to the Master and Hunt Servants and then kept quietly out of their way.

Several of the hounds had been "walked" during the early part of the year by some of their friends, who had thus taken charge of them, and it was interesting to see how they were getting on now that they had been returned to the Kennels.

Merrie, engaged in looking at the pack to see if she could recognize any of them, got too near, and was called to order sharply by Uncle Joe.

"The hounds are intent on their job and on doing what they are told. They may not even notice you if you get too close to them. Don't you let Sambo tread on a hound, my girl, or you'll be sorry. And don't get too near to other horses or let them crowd you— avoid them, get out of the way."

Eventually they reached a big spinney of trees and undergrowth, which was the covert for which they were heading, and the young hounds were soon at work.

Uncle Joe pointed out that they could get a lot of fun listening to and watching the young hounds, and that they could not expect a run as early as this. Just occasionally it happened, or was allowed to happen.

After about half an hour they moved off to another covert, and hounds had to pass quite close to the children who were standing across the track.

"Turn your ponies' heads towards them," said Uncle Joe and they edged into a gateway, carefully turning their ponies so that they faced towards the track along which hounds were about to pass.

"Surely if I just got out of the way without turning round it would do?" asked Merrie.

"No," said Uncle Joe. "It just would *not* do. I am sure Sambo would be the last pony in the world to kick hounds, but you must take no chances *whatever*. It is unlikely that Alexander or Mayflower, both of whom are so quiet with other animals, would kick, but it would be fatal for them to do it once or to get the habit, therefore it is only fair to take every precaution. If they are turned towards hounds, not only are their heels out of the way but they can see them coming."

Just about nine o'clock hounds got on to an old fox, strange to relate, and gave them a short, sharp run—which served to whet the appetites of both the children and the young entry.

They streamed across a couple of fields, Davy nobly holding the gate to let various people through and closing it again after them. Alex was excited and ready to show what he could do if they had a real run. Sambo streaked along, up on to a low bank, jumping a ditch the other side before Merrie, who clutched his mane, realized what was happening. This actually put them in the lead up a stiff hill which had to be climbed.

The fox went to ground in a spinny about half a mile away, and there they found Uncle Joe and Miss Meyrick, who had guessed what would happen and had ridden quietly round.

"This old dog-fox—I guessed it was the same one—gives us this little spin every year, and the Master usually lets hounds have a short trial run."

He glanced at the excited children and their sweating ponies. "You've had enough for to-day. The ground's too hard and the weather too hot for anything but hound work in covert during this part of the cubbing season. That's partly why cubbing starts so early in the morning, before the heat of the day."

Well, the children had at least begun to learn a few things from their early morning outing. To watch hounds at work, to get the meaning of the various sounds, to make way for hounds at all times, to keep out of their way and keep quiet, to show good manners

Sambo facing the hounds as they passed

and good sense in the opening *and* shutting of gates, not to over-ride their ponies or jump unnecessary fences, and to have plenty of restraint and patience at all times.

Uncle Joe made them discuss most of these things with him, reminding them that there were four others they must never forget when real hunting started: (1) to take the greatest care never to ride over growing crops; (2) never to gallop past a herd or flock of other animals; (3) to keep, if possible, down-wind of the pack, since the smell of your horse is less likely to interfere with the scent and it is easier for you to hear what is happening; (4) to be absolutely quiet and still at a check.

He said that in addition to this they must never ride on top of hounds—for one thing it might drive them off the line—and never crowd at a gap, and never fail to rest and help their ponies, jumping off their backs if a long wait seemed likely. (Incidentally, when carrying a hunting whip, which is very useful for many things, including opening gates, hold it a little nearer the handle than the middle, with the thong loosely looped in your hand and the end pointing forwards or sideways, *not* backwards).

The ponies had a short drink at a stream on their way home, and were taken back quietly. Despite this, Mayflower had sweated herself into such a state that they decided to wash her over, get the water off with the scraper, and give her a good wisping over with hay to get her circulation going before they turned her out.

There was no need to look for thorns or gorse prickles, as might have been the case after a winter day's hunting, and the ponies had really had an easy time.

During the next three days Alex and Mayflower had their shoes off, as the two boys would not ride them again until the Christmas holidays. They would have a feed each day and Uncle Joe intended to keep an eye on them and see that their water did not freeze up. They were company for each other and it was hoped to get them ready for some good days' hunting in the Christmas holidays— unfortunately they would miss the October hunter trials, though Merrie talked of going in for the children's events with Sambo.

Actually Merrie, who did not go to boarding school, looked forward to getting ahead with her riding during the winter months, and thought she would catch up easily with the two boys.

Twinkle was now Sambo's devoted friend and Uncle Joe was looking forward to the time when she and Foozalum had grown a bit, when she could be trained and Foozie could ride her.

So we must leave them for the moment—three, no four, happy children (Merrie, Philip, Davy and Foozie) and their contented, clever ponies, Sambo, Alexander, Mayflower and Twinkle. Perhaps we shall be able to follow their adventures on some future occasion.

THE END

APPENDICES
AND
NOTES

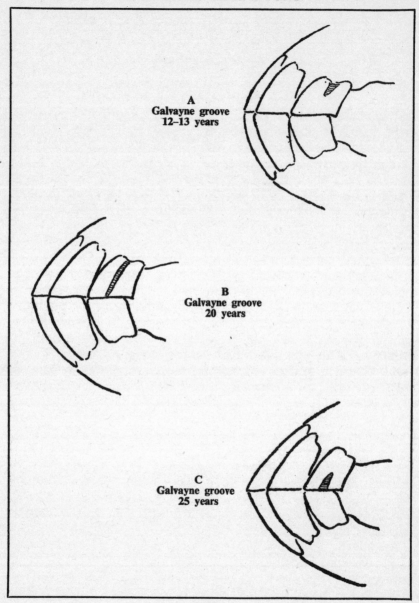

A
Galvayne groove
12–13 years

B
Galvayne groove
20 years

C
Galvayne groove
25 years

APPENDIX TO CHAPTER III

TEETH.—The groove in Sambo's upper corner tooth is called the Galvayne groove and it would look something like diagram A at 12 or 13, at 20 it would look like diagram B, and at 25 like diagram C.

Males have 40 teeth, females 36. The difference is that the mares have no tushes, which are rather odd teeth which appear in the males when they are about four years old but take some time to develop. These tushes grow a little way behind the front teeth or incisors, and a good bit in front of the back teeth, or molars, in that part of the jaw where no teeth are to be seen in the mouth of a mare or filly. They therefore stand by themselves and the male has four of them, one on each side of both the top and bottom jaws.

Foals are born with what are called milk teeth, which are smaller and whiter than the permanent ones.

Since the front teeth in the bottom jaw are the ones usually studied for age we will only speak of these teeth, though it must be remembered that a vet. can obtain a lot of information from the inspection of the upper as well as the back teeth, or molars.

Just before he is three years old a pony loses his two centre milk teeth, and when he is three he has two permanent incisors, right in the middle of the front of the bottom jaw, and two milk teeth on each side of them. The same thing is repeated when he is four with the next two milk teeth, leaving only one milk tooth on each side, which he loses before he is five.

But it is not until he is six that the last two teeth are fully developed. The permanent teeth are slightly hollow in the centre and this is what is called "the mark", which disappears from the two middle ones at seven—it is not that the centre fills up, but that the outside of the teeth has worn down.

The outside corner tooth (not the tush) will be a shell rather than a fully developed tooth at five, perfect at six and with a slight hook at seven.

When the pony is eight the marks will be difficult to find

in the teeth on either side of the centre two, but there will be a short straight line known as the fang hole in front of the place where the mark had been on the centre two, which as he grows older will become just a spot. There will still be a mark on the outside corner teeth, the last to come through, but this will be gone at nine, and the Galvayne groove appears at ten on the upper corner tooth.

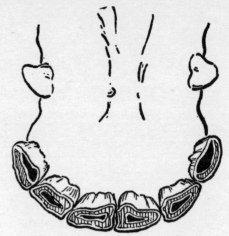

Mouth of six-year-old, showing tables of lower incisors

As their age increases, ponies' teeth become three-cornered rather than oval, and begin to slope in the manner described by Philip. Sometimes the teeth of a very old horse are sloped so much that they do not meet properly, which makes it difficult for him to crop grass.

The molars or back teeth are the ones which occasionally have to be filed. They sometimes grow uneven or jagged through not eating hard food, such as oats.

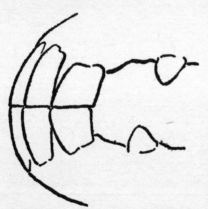

Side view of mouth of six-year-old

**SAMBO'S CONFORMATION
—NECK.**—A pony's neck "which looks upside down" is badly joined at the shoulders.

PASTERN.—This is the bone connecting the fetlock joint and the foot. It should not be too short and upright, as this means jarring, leading perhaps to ringbone. Nor should it be too long and sloping as the pony may catch his foot in rough going, or it may not support the weight properly, eventually sinking.

Faults of Conformation

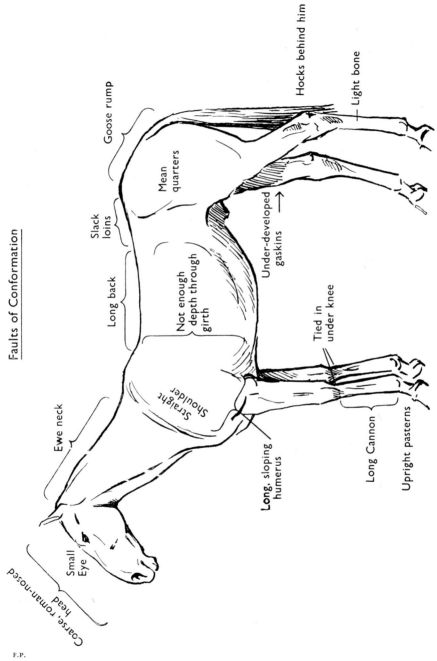

Goose rump

Hocks behind him

Light bone

Mean quarters

Slack loins

Under-developed gaskins

Long back

Not enough depth through girth

Tied in under knee

Ewe neck

Straight Shoulder

Long, sloping humerus

Long Cannon

Upright pasterns

Small Eye

Coarse, roman-nosed head

F.P.

Here is a gag snaffle—the reins through the holes in the rings and up over the horse's head as part of the bridle. There is a dark vulcanite pelham, an ordinary straight bar pelham, a twisted snaffle, a plain pointed snaffle and an egg-but snaffle (the only difference is that the rings are not round but shaped as shown). The inside of a saddle shows how it is padded so as not to injure a horse's back.

Practising touching toes on both sides.

APPENDIX TO CHAPTER VII

The first photo, facing page 44 (not of Sambo but of another pony), shows some of the mistakes Uncle Joe deliberately made when fitting Sambo's saddle and bridle. The second, how they should really look. When correcting the mistakes the first thing he did was to see that the bridle fitted properly—that the bit was not so narrow that it pinched the sides of Sambo's mouth, or so wide that it obviously was too big for him; that the side pieces of the bridle were not buckled so short that the bit was very high in his mouth and cut his lips, or so low that it rattled against his teeth (it should lie on the bars of his mouth where there are no teeth).

Then, he made sure that the noseband lay inside the side pieces, not so low that the action of the bit pressed a little piece of flesh between it and the noseband, thus pinching it, or so high that it rubbed the cheek-bone, or so tight that it caused sores or discomfort—actually about three fingers below the cheek-bone is the right place for it, and as a test for tightness insert the width of three fingers between it and the pony's nose.

Uncle Joe also looked to see if the browband fitted—it might easily be too short, in which case it would pull the head-piece tight against his ears and cause much discomfort and soreness; that the throat lash was not tight enough to interfere with the pony's breathing, or loose enough to be useless.

With regard to the saddle, which Uncle Joe carefully put on rather far forward and then slid back into position, he pointed out that the stirrups must always be run up to the top of the leather, otherwise the irons may swing about, frighten the pony, catch in something or strike the head of anyone who happened to be near.

Uncle Joe then pointed out that the saddle was not so far forward that it could either interfere with the pony's shoulder action, or slip over his withers; or so far back that the rider was sitting on the wrong part of his mount and the girths were round the fatter part of the pony, with the result that if the saddle slipped forward.

H

they would automatically be too loose and it would come round, tipping the rider on to the ground.

The front of the saddle must not touch the pony's withers, or the back of it his spine, even when anyone was sitting on it.

Uncle Joe pointed out that a saddle may look perfectly

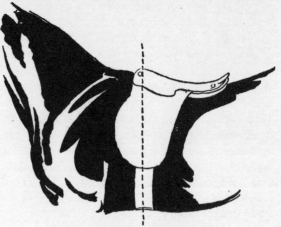

Saddle pressing on withers and spine

all right until it has been ridden in a little while and the rider's weight has brought it right down against the pony, so you must never be content with first glance when using a saddle to which your pony is not accustomed.

There must be an air passage from the front to the back for two reasons, first to keep it from pressing on his spine and causing injury; second, to help keep him cool and comfortable.

The girths must be (a) flat, not twisted or wrinkled; (b) buckled tight enough to keep the saddle from slipping round, but not

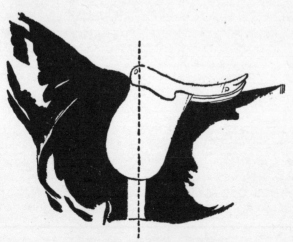

Saddle with sufficient air passage

ridiculously tight (you should put the saddle on the pony's back rather loosely girthed for a few minutes, or longer in cold weather, and then tighten the girths, first making sure the saddle has not moved out of position); the flaps must lie flat each side and the buckle of the girth should lie on them, not on the pony's skin.

If a folded leather girth is used, the fold should point towards the front legs, the two edges towards the back.

The pony's skin must be flat, not wrinkled by the girth. A fat grass-fed pony will often "slim" considerably during a ride on a hot day, in which case the girth should be tightened again while out.

Exercises. At every riding lesson a few minutes were devoted to

Front view of saddle pressing on withers   Front view, showing sufficient clearance

riding without stirrups, with the legs hanging fairly straight, and the arms hanging at each side, or else folded. This was done at the walk only for some time, then at the trot and then the canter. The canter was quite easy, but the ability to do it at the trot should first be acquired before attempting the canter, because of the break from one pace to another.

Alternatively to riding without stirrups the children often rode bareback. Sambo sometimes wore a light rug with a surcingle to hold it in place, sometimes nothing. He had a nice strong back and was not bony to sit on.

Several of the ordinary gymnastic exercises were carried out at each ride, such as:

115

(a) To lean back with folded arms until your head touches the pony's spine (do not move feet or knees).
(b) To stretch your right arm straight above your head, then bring it over with a swinging motion to touch your left toe, followed by a similar move with left arm and right toe.
(c) To place your hands on your hips and swing your trunk half right and half left, keeping, as always, feet and knees in position.
(d) To be led along, either bareback or on a saddle, with your arms alternately folded and held straight above your head.
(e) To practise swinging the legs backwards and forwards, singly and together, with and without the stirrups.

Uncle Joe always persuaded the children to carry out these exercises as correctly and rhythmically as they would in a gym class, as he said they were not very much good otherwise.

With regard to trotting, Merrie "bumped" or sat still in the saddle until she automatically got the "feel" of it, and found herself pressing on her stirrup irons and rising in time to Sambo's movement.

She had to watch three things very carefully:

(1) to keep her hands as still as possible—hands move automatically with the movement of the pony, but they must *never* move because your body or arms are incorrect or unbalanced. As far as you are concerned you must keep them absolutely still. No jerky movements of the hands or arms are ever allowed. They must be like bits of elastic.
(2) To keep her knees close to the saddle and her heels down.
(3) To press on her stirrup irons. This helped her to carry out (2) correctly and to use herself properly, so that she and her pony went well together and she was never a passenger.

APPENDIX TO CHAPTER XI

The pages devoted to tack cleaning were meant to describe the ordinary, everyday work which must not be scamped but needs to be got through as quickly as possible. The noseband and throat lash must always be undone to be cleaned—they should most definitely be undone before they are taken off the pony. About once a month the side-pieces should be unbuckled, in fact every single buckle or loop that you can undo should be straightened out and thoroughly cleaned.

Some people do this every day, but it is rather a lengthy job. They also prefer to leave the stirrup leathers hanging straight from a hook all night, instead of replacing them on the saddle, and to hang up the girths as well.

This makes for a little delay in saddling up the next day, and is to be recommended but is not essential. It is essential, however, to hang up the leathers while they are being cleaned and to take extra trouble over the fold which usually holds the stirrup irons, and to run the irons up when you replace them, otherwise this bit of the leather will wear away.

It is a good thing to give all leather a *very* light coating with castor oil every month or two, and put it on one side for about 48 hours. It can then be polished and used. The castor oil soaks into it and makes it very supple. If it is going to be put away for any length of time it should first have this light dressing of oil and then be covered up.

Tack cleaning can be done quite quickly if you go at it with a will and mean to get through in a certain time, and providing you take the trouble to acquire the knack and that you do it regularly so that nothing gets into a bad condition.

If your pony wears a leather head collar this must be cleaned just as much as a bridle.

APPENDIX TO CHAPTER XIII

A 14 hands 2 ins. pony in *full work* would probably want six or eight pounds of oats, mixed with a couple of pounds of the best chaff or chopped hay, and ten or twelve pounds of hay a day. The addition of a pound or so of chopped carrots adds variety and is very good for the pony. These measurements are only approximate. The *total* weight of feed required would be about twenty-six pounds.

Some animals require more, others less, oats. Many will do better with half the same amount of bran substituted for half the oats. It is difficult to make a hard and fast rule as so much depends on the amount of work done, on whether the pony is used for hunting and on his particular constitution.

If your pony needs less oats you must make up the amounts with something else, with an equivalent amount of the best hay, or with bran, or carrots, or a mixture. Never dock the quantity of hay unless there is a very special reason, merely increase it to replace the missing oats.

A 13 hands 2 ins. pony will not as a rule require as much as his 14 hands 2 ins. brother. A 12 hands 2 ins. seldom needs any oats at all, except for really hard work or consistent hunting and jumping. He would need about eight or ten pounds of hay, with perhaps three or four pounds of bran, mixed with plenty of chaff and a pound or two of chopped carrots or roots. Total weight should be approximately eighteen pounds.

Feeds must always be well-mixed by hand and these amounts should be spread over three or four mealtimes during the day, given at regular intervals and if possible fairly early in the morning, with a final feed of hay as late as is convenient in the evening.

The last meal of oats or whatever it may be, can, if liked, be given at 6 p.m., and the hay at the same time, provided a bucket of water is left handy; but it is best to "hay-up" at 8 or 9 p.m. if this can conveniently be done. Hay is usually given twice a day only, unless, of course, it is the main feed, but this rather depends on how you are spacing out the meals and when the most work is being done. Providing there is plenty to last through the night, you must give it as it best suits your pony's needs and appetite. See that the pony has plenty of time to eat and digest his meals. at least an hour.

Oats must always be decreased if a pony is not working, and must be started gradually, not too suddenly, if he is not accustomed to them, or when he comes in from grass. Begin with a small amount and gradually increase. There are lots of alternative foods that can be used, but there is little to equal oats for hard, fast work.

A feed of grass is always a good thing, and lawn mowings, provided they are given at once and are not allowed to "hot up", and that they do not contain machine oil or rubbish, can be used. If a pony is not turned out to grass, but just being given some occasionally, do not give more at a time than the weight of an ordinary feed. If you have only a few handfuls of lawn mowings, mix them with the feed.

Some boiled linseed once a week is a good thing, about half a pound (less for a small pony) soaked in water all night or even for twenty-four hours, slowly brought to the boil with constant stirring, and simmered for half an hour, will provide a good meal if mixed with bran and chaff. If not first soaked, it must be boiled for at least four hours.

About a pound of crushed barley a day can help to replace oats if necessary. Bread (not mouldy), a few boiled potatoes, raw cabbage leaves and mangolds (uncut) if the pony will learn to eat them that way, can be fed at a pinch.

Oats are best crushed, otherwise the pony may gulp them down too quickly. They should be fresh, clean, not dusty, with plump grains.

An occasional bran mash with a *small* handful of Epsom salts is excellent, and is best given in the evening. The following day the pony should only do very slow, easy work or, better still, be rested and led out for half an hour.

The mash is made by putting a couple of pounds of bran in a bucket with a little salt, and using a piece of wood to mix it with some actually boiling water until it is nice and smooth, but on no account sloppy. Cover with a sack till cool.

119

Rock salt in the manger is much liked.

Several of the native pony breeds are best without any oats at all. The bigger ponies must not be expected to do any fast work if they do not get oats, but must have a lot of the best hay and other foods. Too many oats will make some ponies unmanageable and they will do surprisingly well with a smaller amount or none at all.

Hay must look and smell fresh, not mouldy, and feel crisp and sappy. It is at its best when a year old, and after eighteen months begins to lose goodness. If you are forced to use dusty hay, shake it out well before feeding it. It can even be slightly damped if really necessary—but always shake out the worst dust first. Any mouldy bits must always be thrown away. Some ponies like clover and some meadow hay. The best hay contains several kinds of good grass, such as meadow fescue. If when you open your bale of hay you find anything wrong with it, ask your forage merchant to take it back—he may not know that it was faulty.

If a pony lives out at grass he can do quite a lot of work, providing it is not too fast, and providing he has plenty of time to eat! Good grass is not just long and green—there should be plenty of herbs growing in it.

In some, but not all, fields the goodness is gone from the grass by the middle of the summer, and hay must be fed. This is certainly the case in the winter, when hay and other things as well must be given whether or not you are using your pony.

Never turn a pony out without a companion, if he is to be left alone for any length of time. Never put him in a "horse sick" pasture which has had too many ponies in it for too long, without it being rested, harrowed and grazed by cattle.

Make sure of two things: (1) that there always is plenty of water available, that it has not become dried up in the summer, or frozen in the winter; (2) that there is shelter of some kind, both from the sun and the icy winds, a clump of trees, high hedges, or an old shed.

During the summer, ponies are often kept in stables during the heat of the day and fed, and turned out in the evening for the night. This agrees with them very well, and if the pasture is good will probably save a little something on their feeding bill.

120

The pony at grass all the year round, or during the wintry half of the year, can be cleaned up for riding, but should *not* be groomed as thoroughly as the stabled pony. He requires the thickness of his coat and the natural oils in the hair as a protection. The carefully groomed, the fine-skinned and the clipped pony at grass in the winter all need protection such as that afforded by a New Zealand rug.

It is necessary to stable some thoroughbred ponies during the winter, though others are none the worse for being turned-out, providing the weather is passable. It should always be remembered that even if unclipped they are often so thin-skinned and the hair of their coat is so fine, that in many cases they need a New Zealand rug every bit as much as a commoner pony which is clipped out.

Since a great deal depends on the size and situation of the paddocks available it is difficult to make many hard and fast rules about keeping ponies at grass, and any points not covered in this appendix should be discussed with experts.

FINAL NOTES

If your pony is standing in a miserable heap with his coat staring —all on end—and a dull eye, you may be sure there is something wrong with him. When in doubt, always call a vet.

When you find that he is coughing, *never* allow him to trot or canter fast. With a bad cough you must not work him at all, but if the weather is fair, lead him out for half an hour morning and/or afternoon. It will do him good to get his head down to eat grass, as if his nose is running it will help him to free it.

A pony with a cough and a cold should never drink out of the same bucket as another horse. He should be well rugged up and kept warm and out of draughts if possible, but he definitely needs fresh air and you must use your common sense as to how much you shut his windows or the top of his stable door in cold weather.

There are some good electuaries on the market, unless you know someone who will make one for you. This is a kind of sticky stuff which acts like a cough-lozenge and soothes and helps a lot. It is put on a horse's tongue with a spoon or a flat, wooden stick, and he can have several doses of it in the day. It dissolves slowly in his mouth.

Should your pony have a swollen tummy, is evidently in great pain and perhaps keeps on getting up or down, or trying to throw himself about, he probably has colic. It may become very serious and you should get a vet as quickly as possible. Sometimes a warm blanket round his tummy may help. He should be prevented from lying down, if possible, as he may roll about too much and twist his intestines. About a wineglassful of brandy, gin or whisky in three times that amount of water may help if there is a long delay before the vet arrives. It would have to be given in a bottle at the side of his mouth. In what is called flatulent colic, a quarter to half a pint of linseed oil (according to the size of the pony) may help, but there is more than one type of colic and it is best to be guided by the vet.

Should your pony for any reason be brought home very hot from a ride, you should walk him about till his coat is nearly dry. A rug should not be put on a sweating pony unless there is some hay or straw under it to keep it off his back and allow the air to get in. As soon as he is quite dry, he can be rugged up properly; but if this is done too soon he will make the rug cold and wet.

The same thing applies if the pony gets soaked by rain. He should be scraped dry with a stable scraper and then rubbed with a cloth, before straw is put on his back and then his rug. If you have no scraper, try and get the water off him with twisted hay. Pull his ears gently with your hands to warm and dry them.

Sore places, such as saddle sores or girth galls and mud fever (sometimes called greasy heels, though it is not quite the same thing) can both be treated with white lotion, made of one ounce each of lead acetate, zinc sulphate and alum to a quart of water—any chemist will make it up. The bottle should be well shaken, the liquid dabbed on with a bit of cotton wool and left to dry.

Never attempt to use your pony until the saddle sore or girth gall are completely healed and hardened, or you may have to lay him up for a long while.

Mud fever must be watched for in the winter, as if taken in time it can be dealt with fairly easily; otherwise it may mean you cannot use your pony for several days. Any sign of swelling and sore places which will soon become cracks between the fetlock joint and heel should be treated at once. If it has been left too long it may be necessary to clean and dry the heel very thoroughly and put a bag of bran on the foot for at least twenty-four hours.

Some ponies suffer from thrush, which means that a nasty-smelling liquid oozes out of the frog of their foot. If neglected this can become very serious. Be sure the pony stands in very clean bedding, wash out his foot carefully, and press a little Stockholm tar into the cleft of the frog every day. Salt can be used if there is any delay in getting the Stockholm tar.

If your pony is not in good condition, thin and boxy, with a lifeless coat which seems to be stuck fast to his bones and will not move easily, this may be caused through a lot of things:

123

(1) Not enough to eat—or drink.
(2) The wrong kind of food, irregular mealtimes, and lack of time for digestion.
(3) His teeth want filing, or there is something wrong with them. Sometimes bad teeth are the cause of a pony throwing his head about, or fighting his bit.
(4) Not being warm enough. He may need another rug, or he is standing on a cold floor without enough bedding on it, or he is in a draught. Draughts and fresh air are two quite different things.
(5) Worms. In this case, send for a vet.
(6) Being rushed about, long canters or gallops or trots, without plenty of walking in between. It is very easy to sweat the flesh off a pony, but not so easy to put it on again. If you ride to a show or gymkhana or meet, get off your pony's back and rest him whenever there is a chance. Use your wits. Never bring him in hot. Do not tie him up and leave him in the sun. During the summer ride him as much in the shade as possible during the hot part of the day.

On very cold days a highly bred pony will often go best with a light rug under the saddle if he is clipped out. Never leave your pony standing in the wind, keep him moving about.

The average pulse of a pony is 36-42 beats per minute—usually about 38. His normal temperature is 100° F.(38° C.). He breathes about 9-15 times a minute (average about 12). Watch his flanks if you want to count his breathing.

If ever you have to make some mixture up quickly remember that:

1 teaspoon = 1 drachm or $\frac{1}{8}$ oz.
2 teaspoons = 1 dessertspoon.
2 dessertspoons = 1 tablespoon ($\frac{1}{2}$ oz. or 4 drachms).
4 tablespoons = 1 wineglass (2 ozs.).
3 wineglasses = 1 teacup (6 ozs.).
1 breakfast cup or tumbler = 10 ozs. or $\frac{1}{2}$ pint.

A *piebald* pony is black and white. *Skewbald* is any other colour and white.

124

Other horsey colours are *black, black-brown, brown, bay-brown, bay*. (A bay often has black points—black on the legs, which looks very showy with a fine black mane and tail. You can have bright bay, dark bay and light bay, which includes a mealy bay. Sometimes it is almost red in colour, at others it is more like a chestnut.)

Chestnut. This may be golden, pale and washy, bright or even reddish. The dark chestnuts include liver chestnuts and mahogany chestnuts, and the light chestnuts include sorrel.

Blue Dun. Black skin, mane and tail, blackish coat giving the impression of blue.

Yellow Dun. Yellow pigment in hair, sometimes striped with darker pigment on head and limbs.

Cream. Cream colour coat and pale skin.

Grey. The coat is of black and white hairs, producing many markings, and getting lighter with age.

Blue Roan. Coat black or blackish with white hair in it, giving a blue appearance.

Bay or Red Roan. Coat bay or bay-brown with white hairs.

Strawberry or Chestnut Roan. Chestnut with white hairs.

Whole-coloured means that there are no hairs of any other colour on the head, body or limbs.

The colour of a pony's coat varies to a certain extent with the season—he changes it twice yearly, and it is often deeper in the winter and lighter in the summer. For this reason it is as well to remember that it hardly alters at all just round the muzzle, and this is the best place to look if you want to be sure of his exact colour.

A Star is a white mark on the forehead.

A Stripe is a narrow white mark down the centre of the face, sometimes joined on to a star, sometimes not.

A Blaze is a white mark covering almost the whole of the front of the face.

A Snip is a small white mark near the nostrils.

A Wall-eye means there is a lack of pigment in the iris, and this gives it a blue- or grey-white appearance.

An Eel-mark is a dark line running along the top of the spine.

Zebra marks mean striping on the neck, withers, limbs or quarters.

A hand is four inches.

As you will sometimes hear people speaking of the different kinds of jumps they met with out hunting here is a description of some of them.

Cut and Laid. This is usually a hawthorn hedge of which the unnecessary branches and twigs have been chopped off, and the stems or small trunks cut half-way through so that they can all be bent one way. Some of the branches and stems are twisted together to make a solid hedge or obstacle, which varies in height. It has to be treated particularly respectfully when it has not been trimmed for some time and a lot of new branches have grown up above the old cut and laid.

Bullfinch. This is a hawthorn or other sort of hedge which has not been "cut and laid", and has grown very tall and straggly, well above your head. It is usually necessary to find a good place where your pony can both jump and wriggle through.

Topped Hedge. One which has been cut and flattened, but not bent as in the cut and laid.

Oxer. This is a hedge which has been protected from cattle by a guard rail on one or both sides. A single oxer often has a ditch on one side and a rail or wire on the other. A double oxer may have rails or wire on both sides.

Post-and-Rails. These wooden fences hardly need to be described as they are exactly like their name. Sometimes there is a double post and rails about 10 feet apart which a bold horse will jump as one obstacle, but a pony must prove himself very handy and jump in and out. The rider must indeed be "going with him", otherwise he (the rider) would get very badly left behind if he were not expecting a double jump of this kind.

Many hedges have a ditch either on the take-off or the landing side, and it is for this reason that a good jumping horse or pony must "spread" himself to avoid trouble. This should prevent him from dropping his hind legs in a ditch, or even against a rail.

In some parts of England there are a number of brooks, and in others you will find deep "rhines" for drainage. Some animals will not jump these readily until they get used to them. Then, too, there are stone walls, which *must* be jumped clean, and banks, some of them "blind". By this I mean that they are part wall, part bank and are often over-grown with brambles which may mask a ditch.

There are also obstacles called "Bottoms", which are narrow brooks with a fence on one side. Here again a horse must spread himself whichever way he is jumping it. Supposing the fence was on the take-off side, this would probably entirely hide the brook from him and you would have to ask him to jump wide, sending him on at it fairly fast.

All these obstacles may sound very alarming, but there is nearly always a way round, and in any case they need not be jumped unless hounds are running and unless you and your pony really know how to deal with them. Never use up your pony's energy by "larking over the jumps" unnecessarily. Be ingenious and find an easy part of the fence if you really must go over it, or use the gate—and *shut it* if you are the last through.

In many of the counties hunted by the various packs, the jumping is not difficult, and a clever, handy pony will creep and climb, saving time that a bigger, clumsier horse might well lose. Unfortunately there is often a great deal of wire to be avoided and it is best to follow an experienced person until you know your way round.

When wire is used very extensively for fencing you will often find a space about as long as a gate where wood has been substituted to make it safer to jump. There are also "Tiger Traps"—consisting of a timber jump and, sometimes, a small stream. It is difficult to describe as it varies in different parts of the country.

Always say "Good Day" to the Master when you see him at the Meet, always obey him implicitly and get out of his way quickly. He cannot carry out his work properly unless he is indeed absolute "master" and you should remember when you are first out with hounds that you are serving your apprenticeship to hunting.

Another thing to remember is to shout "ware (pronounced 'war') hole—or harrows—or wire" or anything else which you spot when you are moving off and which might cause an accident to someone behind you. Never forget your manners—to your own pony, to the Hunt officials, to the followers and to anyone you see out.

Here is a list of the different breeds of British Mountain and Moorland ponies and if you want to know more about them it would be best to get in touch with the Secretary of the National Pony Society, 76 Kew Road, Richmond, Surrey, who will no doubt give you the names and addresses of the secretaries of the societies which look after each breed.

Highland. These ponies are very strongly made, carry themselves proudly and stand about 13 hands 3 ins. to 14 hands 2 ins. Many are of unusual and lovely colours such as golden, silver, fox, dun or mouse and often have silver or black manes and tails.

Fell. Here is another powerful pony about 14 hands in height, with strong, well laid-back shoulders. They are very sure-footed and were used to carry the lead and slate from the mines in the Fells of the Lake District and Northumberland to the sea ports.

Dales. These come from the upper Dales of Tyne, Allen, Wear and Tees and they, too, carried lead to the ports. They are great trotters.

New Forest. Here we have a certain amount of variety in size and type, as New Foresters vary from 12-14 hands or more. Some are very much the riding pony, others ideal for the smallholder.

Connemaras. These are bred in both Ireland and England and are more often grey than anything else, standing from 13-14 hands.

Exmoors. Although smaller (12 hands 2 ins.) the Exmoors are extremely strong, sturdy and courageous—they should never be fed oats. A wide forehead, good eye and mealy nose, plus small, pointed ears are among their chief characteristics.

Dartmoors. A Dartmoor should not be more than 12 hands 2 ins. although he is so well proportioned he can carry a surprising amount of weight. They make excellent children's ponies and the pony record high jump, was, I believe, registered by a Dartmoor.

Shetlands. Very tiny and very strong, these little animals vary from nine hands to 10 hands 2 ins. and are used as both saddle and pack ponies in the Shetland Isles.

Welsh. There are two types of Welsh Mountain Pony nowadays, the small native pony measuring up to 12 hands, who has retained his size and characteristics, and the riding type whose height is not over 13 hands 2 inches, and in whom there is often some Arab blood. Their wild, natural life has made them clever and handy, and they are so well made they can carry out most jobs efficiently.